BETWEEN

AND

A SOFT PLACE

Selected Works

By

Renée Bess

FLASHPOINT
PUBLICATIONS

ISBN 978-1-949096-34-7

Cover Design by AcornGraphics

Editors Verda Foster and Nann Dunne

FLASHPOINT
PUBLICATIONS

Acknowledgments

Thank you, my dearest Vivian, for continuing to honor my literary pursuits, for being my beta listener, for creating such a beautiful yard and garden for me to gaze upon in between the words I type. That we found ourselves in the same place and at the same time so many years ago was serendipitous. That we are still "we" is one of life's miracles.

Thank you, Stephanie for coming back to the U.S. when you did. We've always been closer than the thousands of miles that separated us physically for twenty-one years. We are still close. You are my wonderful, treasured sister.

Thank you, Patty Schramm, for your encouragement. You've been my cheerleader from afar. I appreciate your generous spirit, your empathy toward others, and your command of everything you do.

Thank you, Lori L. Lake, for suspecting my contributions to the body of LGBTQ writing would be worthy, and for inviting me to submit *"Breaking Jaie"* to Regal Crest Enterprises, LLC.

Thank you, Verda Foster and Nann Dunne. Your skillful editing never fails to improve my writing. You epitomize editorial excellence.

Praise for Between A Rock and A Soft Place

The title itself, *Between a Rock and a Soft Place*, conjures up the magic of this book. A mélange of poetry, essays, memoir, prose, short stories infused with sweet insight, savory language, and spicy self-revelation. As a self-professed-Shy with a capital "S"-introvert, Bess generously offers the reader many glimpses into her inner life, and I was left breathless by her courage.

What is at first evident is Ms. Bess's breadth of interests. In these works, we travel from Paris, to the lower level of a mortuary, to the voting polls, to the movies, and to a few bars where she offers her observations on hypocrisy, grief, empowerment, irony, and the labels we yearn to accept or reject.

Between a Rock and a Soft Place starts off with a set of powerful short stories focusing on women coming into their own—often finding love and freedom, but in one case unable to shake the despair of loss. Many of the stories have a black, or mixed-race protagonist aware of, and grappling with, navigating as "the other".

The poems are rife with luscious language. The poignant, *Note Found on the Floor*, a rumination on an absence from writing, declares: "All the poetry is mowed down." In the book's title poem, this line leapt out at me: "Most days I confront the rain and dare the pebble-sharp drops to send me in search of shelter. I don't rust when I'm wet." The poem *No Love Song* reads, "This is not a romance poem, not a tale following a formula that must end happily." The same can be said for this new offering by Bess.

Between a Rock, and a Soft Place is anything but formulaic. Within its pages is a satisfying literary mix. Equal parts wisdom, humor, and homage. I love this collection.

~ Cheryl Head, Award Winning Author of the Charlie Mack Motown Murder Mystery Series

If you enjoy honest, graceful writing, read the long-awaited new book from Renée Bess, *Between a Rock and a Soft Place*. Her short stories, often of reconciliation, will pierce your heart with arrows of gladness and sometimes spears of self-recognition. Her essays explore both the historical and the current as they passionately address racism's unforgivable although repairable damage inflicted upon the oppressed as well as the oppressors. To round out her collection, Bess shares a smattering of her highly personal, heartfelt poetry, a pleasant and thought-provoking read.

~Lee Lynch. Award Winning Lesbian Author

Through prose, poetry and exposition, Renee Bess shows us what it looks and feels like for a Black girl to come out, and for a Black woman to navigate life as a lesbian often rejected by family and the white lesbian world. The stories are historical and contemporary, and occasionally startling. The poems are self-affirming, sassy, and slyly humorous.

The expository writing is clear-eyed, factual, and challenging. What an unusual book! It is to be savored.

There is much to be learned in this book, and much to be felt. Between A Rock and Soft Place indeed.

~ Penny Mickelbury, Award Winning Author

Foreword

I've heard it's best to begin a writing career when one is young. To begin writing very early in life (as soon as possible after learning to hold a pencil or crayon) gives a writer time to learn her craft and reflect upon amateurish errors.

I began writing seriously in mid-life, not during that period's crisis, but in the midst of a catharsis. I've continued to learn the craft, and God knows, every time I reread my work I find and try to correct amateurish mistakes.

I persist because I love the beautiful plasticity of language and the complicated ways of human behavior. I've learned to let my characters take me where they must go. I've continued to write as an act of gratitude for all the authors whose books have taken me away from myself and delivered me to other places and others' truths.

Unlike my previous five books, this one isn't a novel. It's a collection of short fiction, poetry, and creative nonfiction. The first and second genres are a homecoming to and celebration of the writing I first produced. The third genre is rather new to me. It arrived when I most needed to be able to express ideas about the rapidly changing world that surrounds us.

I hope each reader will allow me to hold her/his/their hand in mine as we venture to other places while they read these pieces.

R.B. 2020

Table **O**f **C**ontents

SHORT FICTION

POEMS

OPINIONS AND ASSORTED THOUGHTS

SHORT FICTION

AT THE BEAUTY PARLOR:
WE CAN'T ALWAYS BE STRAIGHTENED

Terez looked down and stared at the chipped linoleum with its interrupted swirls of chocolate-brown and tan. She found it easy to become lost in thought when she concentrated on the different patterns the tiles made. She tried to be interested in the gossip, but nothing made much sense to her because she didn't know the people about whom the operators uttered, "Uh-huh," and "I coulda' told you that two months ago."

She felt a light tap on her shoulder and heard the shampoo lady's familiar voice.

"Come on back, honey. I'm ready for you," Marlene said.

Marlene hummed along with the song on the radio as she squeezed the shampoo bottle until it spurted three or four blobs of thick, gelatinous soap onto Terez's head. Her strong, thick fingers transformed the viscous mixture into suds that she spread from the top of Terez's forehead to the nape of her neck.

As one song spun to the next, Marlene's closed-lip humming kept right up with it. Unfortunately, her fingers felt compelled to match the music's tempo, and before long, Terez felt a jolt as her neck left the curve of the shampoo bowl and, without missing a beat, hit it again. This synergy of the music with Terez's neck repeated a few more times until Marlene pulled the short hose from its perch and began to rinse away the soap, which by now was the consistency of Cool Whip.

Relieved that she'd escaped a concussion, Terez flicked away the tiny trail of water making its way down the side of her face.

Marlene interrupted her humming long enough to grab a small towel and staunch the rivulet before it reached Terez's chin.

"Okay, hon." Marlene dispatched Terez to the one hair dryer that wasn't already in use.

The operator closest to the vacant dryer approached and pulled down the torture instrument's metal hood until it covered Terez's head.

Next to having the hair closest to her ears straightened, a process that sometimes resulted in a singed earlobe, followed by two days of applying cocoa butter or Cuticura to the hot comb's teeth marks, having to sit under the dryer was Terez's least favorite part of her trip to the beauty parlor. The instrument's hot, dry air always made her think about Lawrence of Arabia and camels. Its noise made it impossible to hear the TV's soap opera characters. What was worse, she couldn't read her ever-present book because the dryer's hood prevented her from looking down at the pages.

The only saving grace was not being seated across from Mrs. I'm-Just-Here-For-A-Wet-Set Smith. Today, she'd avoid the opinionated stare this customer seemed to save exclusively for her. If she didn't click her tongue and pass judgment about all the teen-agers she knew, Mrs. I'm-Just- Here-For-A-Wet-Set Smith would ask if Terez's mother approved of her wearing slacks to school instead of skirts.

That's when Terez's operator, Toni, would assume the role of defensive end.

"Of course, she approved of her daughter's outfit," Toni said. "After all, Terez's mother is a teacher and she has very high standards."

Terez never had to say a word to Mrs. I'm-Just-Here-For-A-Wet-Set Smith. That was a good thing, because among her mother's high standards was the prohibition of giving backtalk to adults.

After today's week in the Sahara without shade from the sun or water to drink, Terez moved from the dryer to the chair at Toni's station where the fragrance of burning hair mixed with pomade welcomed her. Usually, about the time one side of Terez's hair was straightened, Toni would pose the same set of questions.

"How's school? Do you really like going to an all-girls school? When do you get to meet boys? Where do you go to meet boys?" And according to the month or season, "Are you going to any Halloween/Birthday/Christmas/New Year's Eve/Valentine's Day parties?"

Terez always delivered her short answers with the flattest tones she could summon.

"All right." "It's fine." "At parties." "Yes," or "No," (depending upon the truth).

Once in a blue moon, Jimmy, the local salesman, would burst through the door.

"Good afternoon, ladies," he'd say with his high-pitched voice.

Jimmy was thin and wiry, all energy. Impeccably groomed, he always arrived carrying a giant suitcase or an assortment of jumbo plastic bags. Today he retreated to the shampoo alcove. One by one, each of the operators left her station and followed him. If an operator failed to inspect Jimmy's merchandise, she was probably short on cash and long on credit.

Sometimes a few of the parlor's customers made the pilgrimage to see what Jimmy had to offer. If their purchases were indicative of Jimmy's stock, Terez knew she'd never be interested. It would be years before cigarettes, bath towels, and bed linens would interest her.

On this particular day, Terez noticed something unusual. All the women in the parlor were less interested in buying something from Jimmy or according reverential silence to the TV. The four operators, Marlene the shampoo lady, and the other three customers, two watching themselves in mirrors and the third bowing her head to accommodate the meet-up of the clipper with the hairline on her neck, seemed more interested in sharing a conversation directed at the same topic.

"Well, if you ask me, I always thought there was something a little different in the way Ms. Rollerson walks," said Mrs. I'm-Just-Here-For-A-Wet-Set Smith, her steel jaw clamped in place like a rusted hull of a ship.

"Oh, come on," Marlene said. "Y'all can't tell anything 'bout a person based on how they walk."

Terez felt heat rise to her face.

"Yes, you can," Toni said. "Plus, she always gets her hair cut so short. Sometimes she doesn't want it straightened, just curled, or maybe some waves. Makes her look mannish."

Toni put her fingertips on Terez's right temple to signal she was ready to sear and straighten the last quarter of Terez's hair.

"Don't start sweatin' in the head, sweetheart, or we'll have to start all over again," Toni cautioned. "Your hair's gonna revert before I can finish straightening it."

Cheryl, a young stylist who'd worked in the beauty parlor for less than a year added, "I did Miz Rollerson's hair once. She kept looking at me in the mirror and smilin'. Asked me why I'd put blonde tips in my hair. She might have called herself paying me a compliment, but she made me feel kinda funny. I'm glad she's not one of my regular customers. She made me nervous."

"Oh, come on, Cheryl," Toni said. She put one hand on Terez's shoulder and wrapped the other around the handle of a curling iron. "You think she's gonna ask you out on a date or something?"

"You never know, Toni. You never know," Cheryl said.

Terez unfurled her fists and pressed her sweaty palms against her thighs, her hands concealed by the smock she was wearing. She looked at her reflection in the mirror and tried to guess how many more tugs of the curling iron she'd have to endure.

The brass bell hanging above the parlor's front door jangled with the arrival of another customer. Conversation ceased.

"Come on back, Ms. Rollerson. I can shampoo you right now." Marlene fixed her gaze on each of the women in the parlor, as if she were daring them to say a word.

Terez watched the newest arrival.

Ms. Rollerson didn't walk. Rather, she strode the length of the beauty parlor, her handsome head held erect. Just short of the shampoo alcove, she paused and turned around to look at Toni.

"Good afternoon, Toni. I forgot to phone and tell you my appointment won't take as long as it usually does. I don't want it straightened, just trimmed and styled in an afro. Who knows? I might not ever get it straightened again."

Ms. Rollerson didn't give Toni a chance to answer, but she did give Terez a quick wink.

Terez swallowed and then began to breathe again.

Framed by the alcove's doorway, Ms. Rollerson turned and looked back at Toni. "I hope that's okay with you. I don't want to mess up your schedule."

"That's not a problem, Ms. Rollerson."

Toni gave Terez a pat on the back. "You're all finished, honey."

Terez rescued her bookbag from its resting place next to Toni's station and fingered the money to pay for her hairdo.

"Thanks, sweetheart. Same appointment time two weeks from now?" Toni asked.

"Yes, please." Terez felt two one-dollar bills that remained in her pocket. "I have to go back and tip Marlene."

Striding instead of walking, Terez went back to the shampoo area.

"Bye, Marlene," she said. "I wanted to give you this."

"Thanks, baby. My hands are fulla soap. Here, just put it in my pocket."

Between Marlene and Terez lay Ms. Rollerson, her head resting on the shampoo bowl, her eyes closed. As Terez reached over and placed the tip in Marlene's apron pocket, Ms. Rollerson opened her eyes and smiled.

"See you in two weeks, sugar," Marlene said.

Terez left the shampoo area and approached Toni.

"Toni, could you please write 'shampoo and afro' next to my name in your appointment book?"

Toni howled. "That's okay with me, but are you gonna check with your mother?"

"No, I don't think so."

Terez flashed a conspiratorial smile and strode to the front door, stepping over the irregularly shaped tan and chocolate-brown linoleum tiles.

THREE TRUTHS AND ONE SECRET

Six days after leaving her home in Philadelphia and finding her way to the Port of New York City, Alma Clay grabbed her suitcase's handle and joined the line of third-class passengers disembarking the *SS Leviathan*. She'd been planning her departure from home for quite a while. Self-assured, Alma didn't fear traveling by herself, not even to a foreign country. She'd read extensively about France, Paris in particular. And her aunt's letters described places so well, she expected she'd recognize certain streets, parks, and stores on first sight.

No, France didn't intimidate her. In fact, venturing toward that which was new attracted her just like a magnet drawn to a piece of metal.

Alma stepped over the last of the raised rungs nailed crossways on the ship's wooden walkway. As her feet touched solid ground, she looked up at the leaden sky and silently said a prayer of gratitude for having crossed the Atlantic Ocean safely and in one piece. There had been only one touchy incident, but she'd handled herself and the obnoxious man and his wife satisfactorily. Alma followed the phalanx of passengers as they made their way to the Customs and Immigration Office.

The gray sky gave in to rain, a soft, fine mist that Alma welcomed as the moisture kissed her face.

The line of her fellow passengers grew shorter as some people siphoned off to the left toward a sign that read, *"Citoyens de L.R.F."*

Alma remained where she was, surrounded by voices speaking all sorts of languages. The tide of different inflections washed over her ears, arriving full, and then diminished as they receded. She adjusted quickly to the sounds of male voices blending with female tones and the high-pitched staccato notes flying from the mouths of

children. There was something about the richness of this
noise that wrapped around Alma's shoulders and reminded
her that she was at the borderline of a new reality.

Alma Clay was now in the port city of Cherbourg,
France. America was almost a week and definitely a sea
away.

In her refusal to be cowed by her realization, Alma read the
words posted on another sign: *"Passagers d'Outre-Mer."*

She watched many of her fellow passengers, including
other English-speaking Americans, veer toward that sign, so
she did as well. In no time at all she was at the front of the
line. When summoned forward by a man wearing a black
jacket, pristine white shirt, black tie, and hat accented by a
bill that was both broad and shiny, Alma approached the
small wooden structure where he sat.

"Bonjour, Mademoiselle. May I see your passport and
arrival papers?"

Alma handed him her documents.

The immigration officer opened Alma's passport,
turned to the page that bore her photo, and alternately
looked at her and her likeness.

"You are a citizen of the United States?" he asked.

"Yes."

"And where do you live?"

"I live in Philadelphia."

He nodded as he flipped through each page of Alma's
passport.

"What is your address?"

"One hundred twenty-five North Fiftieth Street."

"And what is the purpose of your visit in France?"

Alma recalled her aunt's directions about answering
such questions.

"I'm a journalism student, and I've come here to
research life for Americans who are living in Paris."

Barely waiting to hear Alma's last syllable, the customs
agent exhaled another question. "How long do you plan to
stay in France, Mademoiselle?"

This time Alma delivered her aunt's coached response
verbatim. "For a month, or maybe two."

The officer stamped Alma's passport and immigration

document and handed her the former. "Welcome to France, Mademoiselle Clay."

He inclined his head forward, politely dismissing her.

"Thank you." Alma turned to her right and started to walk away. Suddenly she stopped.

"Oh, could you tell me where I can get the train to Paris?" she asked.

"Certainly, Mademoiselle." The officer pointed toward large doors at the other end of the Customs and Arrivals Hall.

"Leave by that exit and look to the left. You'll see a large building with an open roof. That is the train shed."

"Merci, Monsieur." Alma smiled coquettishly and began walking the length of the cavernous hall.

Once she was outside, she saw the train building at the end of a long cobblestone path, now made slick by the rain. Despite her shoes' subtle heels, common sense warned Alma to pay attention and step cautiously. The last thing she wanted to do was fall and twist her ankle or break a bone, any bone.

She felt her left foot slide forward too quickly for her right foot to follow. Giving in to gravity, she swung her suitcase behind her to soften the backward fall that didn't happen.

"Dammit!" she said.

The near accident sealed her determination to concentrate on the cobblestone's patterns. She knew there had to be a trick to keeping her balance. What if all the streets in Paris were paved like this path?

The walk to the train shed was a short one. Alma entered the cavernous structure and glanced at its oval glass ceiling, grayed with layers of soot that pre-dated the steam engines and abetted by today's rain-filled clouds. She spotted a row of ticket windows with their destinations clearly posted. Le Havre, Rouen, Les Andelys, names she'd looked at each time she'd examined her worn map of France. Near the middle of the row of ticket booths were two lines of travelers awaiting their turn to pay the fare for a ride to Paris.

She tightened her fingers around her suitcase's handle

and joined one of the lines of Paris-bound ticket buyers. In front of her stood a well-dressed man, his overcoat draped neatly over one arm. The woman next to him was also well-dressed.

The man turned slightly and saw Alma standing in his shadow.

Somewhat startled, he looked down at her.

"*C'est vous encore.* It's you, again," he said. His mustachioed upper lip spread into a snarl.

Taken aback for a second, Alma stood erect, determined to equal the man's height. She glared at him and hoped her eyes and the set of her mouth would wither his hostility.

"Yes. It's me again."

The woman turned and looked at Alma. She quickly swung back around and faced the ticket booth.

The man scowled silently before turning toward the woman and showing Alma the back of his carefully tailored suit.

The line of ticket buyers crept forward slowly as Alma resurrected the two-day old memory of her previous encounter with this couple.

Two evenings ago, in violation of the rules that segregated the *SS Leviathan's* passengers according to the price they'd paid for their ticket, Alma ventured from her third-class area to one of the decks designated for first-class passengers. She'd heard all sorts of tales about the monied passengers. Some traveled with their maids, valets, and nannies. A few of the older, infirm first-class passengers brought along their private nurses. Curious about their staterooms, dining rooms, men-only smoking lounges, children's playrooms, and parlors, Alma decided to enter this new territory to see whatever she could of the ship's forbidden areas. She was careful and avoid being discovered.

She climbed what seemed to her like a million steps in a never-ending stairwell that began mid-deck in the third-class area of the ship and ended at the first-class promenade deck. She pushed open a door and stepped out onto the wide deck. It smelled of sea air and wood polish. A regiment of deckchairs was interrupted here and there by the protrusion of cubby-hole closets, no doubt filled with blankets for those passengers who were sufficiently hardy to ensconce themselves in a deckchair during the fall and winter crossings.

Alma stepped closer to the deck's railing. She looked to her left and right and saw no one there. Total absence was what she'd hoped for as the first-seating diners were enjoying the evening meal and the second-seating passengers were dressing for dinner or sipping their pre-dinner drinks in one of the lounges.

Alma walked one-third of the deck's perimeter before her exploration came to a halt. She saw a door open and suddenly found herself facing a man and woman. Her mind raced. Should she portray servility, or brave and mind-your-business?

"Excuse me, Mademoiselle."

The tuxedo-clad man spoke as he and his female companion approached Alma. "You do know this deck is for first-class passengers only, don't you?"

"Of course I do," Alma answered, her voice steady.

"Well then, why are you here?"

"I'm here to enjoy the evening air," Alma said.

The man stared at her. "You're enjoying the evening air?" he asked, his voice filled with incredulity.

"Yes. In fact, I'm enjoying the entire crossing."

The man's eyes narrowed to slits.

"How much can one enjoy a crossing while traveling in third class? Or is it steerage?" he asked.

"Oh, much more than my relatives enjoyed their trip across the ocean." Alma paused. "They were shackled in leg irons, and they didn't have a choice of dinner seatings. They became sick to their stomachs and sick in their hearts when they cried for the places and people they'd never see again."

The woman gasped, "Oh, Hervé!"

The man put his hand under her elbow, as if to steady her.

"There's nothing to worry about, Bette."

He squared his shoulders and faced Alma.

"I'll make sure the first officer knows about your intrusion into this area," he said.

As Alma took a step backward, the woman stared at her

intently and then quickly looked away.

"Go ahead and report me," Alma said. "In the meantime, I'm going to enjoy this fresh air. It's liberating. Just like freedom."

Alma left the pair of upper-class passengers in her wake and continued her circuit around the first-class promenade deck. She hoped they couldn't see her holding her breath as she retreated. She held in every molecule of oxygen until she found the staircase she'd used earlier and began her return trek down the steps that ended in a passageway to the third-class area.

She walked past the ship's laundry and inhaled the odor of lavender-infused steam mixed with human sweat. Women's voices got folded within the dress shirts, trousers, and bed linens that fell prey to the industrial iron presses. The voices reminded her of her Aunt Vangie's description of the French laundry where she worked when she first arrived in Paris.

"I hated it there," Aunt Vangie wrote in a letter to Alma. "Being a dishwasher in a bistro is a better job for me, Alma."

When Alma returned to the *SS Leviathan's* two-berth quarters she shared with an older female passenger, she went directly to the wash basin and splashed water on her face.

Then she pulled her suitcase from its nest below her bed and extracted the pile of letters that traveled with her. She had arranged them in chronological order, starting with the oldest, written two springs ago, and ending with the latest one, penned ten days prior to her departure for France.

Slowly she reread her aunt's first letter.

Vangie, or Evangeline as her former employer always called her, was the younger sister of Alma's mother, Ethel. Vangie, or "You're-a-disgrace-to-our-family" as Ethel usually addressed her sister, was Alma's sole and adored aunt. Vangie knew that trios sometimes formed two-against-one coalitions, and although the design of those coalitions could be fluid, it seemed to Vangie that she and her niece Alma were usually united in opposition to her sister Ethel.

When Vangie announced her intention to leave Philadelphia

and live in France, Alma felt crushed under the boulder of losing a beloved ally before she'd had a chance to figure out the whys and wherefores of her own existence. Who would defend her when she spoke about the importance of books and her desire to be a writer? Who would smile indulgently each September when she described the beauty of her favorite teacher? And who would scoff at her mother's annoyance because Alma's favorite teachers were always females?

"You want to be a writer?" her mother asked. "That's no way to make a living."

"Now, Ethel. You don't know that for sure," countered Aunt Vangie. "Your daughter writes well. She could go far in life with her name printed on book covers."

"She'd go farther in life if she had her name next to an employed man's on a marriage certificate."

At that point, Aunt Vangie would always go silent, glance at Alma, and eke out a smile she meant to be consoling or at least understanding.

Alma always interpreted her aunt's smile as all-knowing, even though Alma wasn't quite sure what all Vangie knew, just as she didn't know why her mother considered Vangie such a disgrace to the family.

But now, here she was, Alma Clay, the first college graduate in her family. She wanted to become a writer. She was as determined to be a writer as she was to accept her aunt's long-standing invitation to come to Paris where she might find opportunities that were nonexistent in the world of Philadelphia in 1928.

Alma smoothed the crease in the middle of the letter and read it once again.

March 25, 1926

My Dear Niece,

I am still here in Paris, happy, healthy, and employed. The last two years have passed by so quickly. While you've continued your studies, I've gone from being a laundress to a dishwasher in a small restaurant, then a server in an after-hours watering hole, and now a combination hostess

and barman in a swanky jazz club. I said "barman" because
in Paris it's rare to be served drinks or meals by a woman.

I feel like I'm sitting on top of the world every night
when I come to work. All the club-goers...how they do
dress! And the music swings. Guess what? When colored
and white patrons dance together in the club, I'm the only
one who seems to notice it. There are a lot of Negro
ex-soldiers who stayed in France after the war ended. They
learned to speak French and got jobs and places to live.
Some of them found wives. Life here is better for us, Alma.
Most of the Parisians don't look at you like you shouldn't
be walking on the same side of the street with them.

Lately, I've struck up conversations with some of the
regulars at the club. They're Negro Americans just like me,
except they're painters and musicians and writers. They tell
me they feel freer here to paint and compose and write than
they felt in the U.S. A few have told me other things about
other kinds of freedom. All that makes me think about you,
Alma. If you still want to be a writer, maybe you should
come to Paris.

Think about it, honey, and start saving money. I'll stash
away some of my salary for you every week. That way, I can
help you pay for a steamship ticket in another year or so.

Tell your mother "You're-a-disgrace-to-our-family"
says "Hi."

Love,

Aunt Vangie

Train ticket in hand, Alma stopped in front of the large
board where a uniformed man was posting the trains'
numbers, destinations, departure times, and platform
designations. She waited for him to add the information for
her Paris-bound train and then searched the train shed's
perimeter until she spotted the sign for the correct platform.

As she approached the platform, she saw passengers
already boarding. Well ahead of her were the hostile man
and woman. The pair was headed toward the front of the
train, no doubt to the "Première Classe" cars.

Alma knew her third-class train ticket guaranteed she didn't need to worry about being seated anywhere near the troublesome, snotty couple. She did wonder, though, if her Aunt Vangie had it right about France being different from the United States, because so far, she'd been reminded in no uncertain terms that she belonged to a class lower than the upper crust. And the reminders had been based upon race-conscious supposition, not fact.

Alma stepped onto a third-class car and selected a well-worn seat next to a window. She opened her bag and removed the stack of letters her aunt had written to her. There was one letter in particular that she'd reread countless times.

Its first page was filled with Aunt Vangie's anger regarding the rejection notes Alma had received in response to her job applications. Not one daily newspaper within five hundred miles of Philadelphia was interested in hiring her. The many articles she'd written for the Temple University News meant nothing. Her writing and editorial experience were eclipsed by her gender and race.

The hiring committee at the *Pittsburgh Courier* said just as much in returning her application and expressing their desire to "avoid their readers' and advertisers' negative and perhaps punitive reactions to [their] publication" if they were to employ her.

The second page of her aunt's letter contained a confession of sorts along with an invitation.

The time has come for me to explain myself to you, Alma. To share two of my truths. Do you remember Charles Mercer, the guy I used to date shortly after the war ended? Charles was in the Army during the war and his unit was sent here, to France. He used to tell me all kinds of things about this country, and I always got the impression that he liked it here much better than in the States. One day he told me exactly why he favored being in France. He'd always preferred the company of other men more than women. That kind of thing was more tolerated here than in America, or even in England, where to my ears most of the men sounded like they were that way. Charles said that in France they wouldn't put you in jail if they found out that you were homosexual, or "gay," as they say here.

So, after Charles told me all about himself, he said he felt he could trust me with his secret because he suspected I might be gay as well. I denied it at first. I'd denied it ever since I'd had my first crush on a female schoolmate. Charles helped me understand there was nothing wrong with loving a person who's the same sex as you. He believes we're born with those tendencies. I've come to believe that, too.

I think everyone has at least three truths that see the light of day when the time is right. My first truth is that I love women. My second truth is that my loving women does not make me inverted or mentally sick, and I won't be shamed into hiding who I am. My third truth is one that few people, especially few Americans, experience. I plan to share that truth with you as soon as you arrive.

And now, just as Charles showed me the way to my first truth, I'm giving you the key to yours, dearest Alma. I believe you are gay, or more specifically, a lesbian. Perhaps you've already discovered this, perhaps not. In your letters you never mention you're seeing anyone, so it's possible you haven't acknowledged this truth about yourself. Just know that it's safe to be who you are. Your heart's desire won't bump into obstacles here, just acceptance.

Love always,

Aunt Vangie

Alma folded the letter and tucked it back into place with the others. She looked through the window at the passing landscape of fields abloom with yellow rapeseed plants and distant poplars standing guard over narrow roads. She blended the realism of her failed relationship with Laura, the young woman she'd met in college, with daydreams of the two of them being strong enough to love each other fully, openly. The daydreams melted into real dreams as Alma gave way to her exhaustion and slept for the remainder of the rail journey to Paris.

"Paris! La Gare St. Lazare! Paris!"

The conductor's raspy voice announced the train's arrival.

Alma gathered her handbag and suitcase. With the train barely at a standstill, she stepped onto the platform and followed the throng of people headed toward stairs that would lead them to the station's exit and out to the streets of Paris's 8th *arrondissement*.

Alma spotted a line of taxicabs across the street from the train station. She approached the first taxi and spoke to the driver through the taxi's open window.

"Sixteen... I mean *rue Clauzel, numéro seize, s'il vous plaît.*"

The driver nodded.

Five minutes and a tangle of diagonal streets later, the cab stopped in front of Alma's destination. She withdrew two multicolored paper francs from her purse and paid for the ride. As she gripped her suitcase, she remembered her aunt's instructions.

Alma pushed open the huge wooden door with the number sixteen affixed to it and looked through the entrance's short tunnel to a small sunlit courtyard. She followed the cobblestone path as it veered to the left and stopped in front of a coffee-brown painted door, which was smaller than the first one. She lifted the tarnished, pitted knocker and smacked it against the wood.

A voice unlike her aunt's answered.

"J'arrive!"

The door swung open and revealed a rather plump, brown woman wearing a smile.

"You're, Alma, right?" she asked.

"Yes, I am."

"I am Claudine, your Aunt Vangie's good friend. She asked me to be here to meet you."

Claudine's words, spoken in French-accented English, sounded like musical notes.

"She's not here?"

"No, but come in and I'll explain to you where she is."

Alma entered the apartment's dimly lit foyer.

"Please give me your suitcase, and I'll take it to your room."

With Claudine and her luggage out of sight, Alma glanced at her surroundings. She saw a table in what she surmised was the living room. It held framed photos of her aunt, smiling and in the company of others who looked equally happy. She noticed her own rather serious expression captured months ago when she posed for her graduation portrait. Before she could look any further, Alma heard footsteps approaching.

Just as Claudine reappeared, Alma spotted a photo of Aunt Vangie and a woman, both dressed in slacks, and standing close to each other. Vangie's grin was so contagious that Alma found herself smiling at the picture. Although Alma looked at the photo for less than a few seconds and despite the other woman looking more like a silhouette because her face was turned toward Vangie, a fleeting sense of familiarity drifted through Alma's consciousness, a half-thought that became subsumed into Claudine's voice.

"I would offer you a cup of tea, but Vangie is eager to see you," she said.

"I'm anxious to see her also." Alma stared at Claudine. "Where is she?"

"Come with me. It's easy to get a taxi from here." Claudine opened the door. "I'll explain everything to you."

Alma followed Claudine through the small courtyard, the covered entry tunnel, and out to the street. Claudine waved her hand toward a nearby taxi. She leaned past the cab's open window and spoke to the driver.

"L'Hôpital Pitié Salpêtrière, s'il vous plaît."

Once they'd settled into the backseat of the taxi, Claudine turned to Alma.

"A week ago, Vangie was leaving the nightclub where she works. As soon as she stepped onto the street, she was struck by an automobile. Gérard, a man who works at the club with her, saw it all happen. Thank God he was there. He ran back into the club and called for the police. When the police arrived, Vangie was unconscious. They took her to the hospital, and Gérard went with them. He knew your aunt couldn't speak, and even if she could, her French is far from perfect." Claudine paused and leaned forward.

"S'il vous plaît, Monsieur. L'entrée du nord," she said to the taxi driver.

"Bien sûr, Madame."

Fear banished all of Alma's curiosity about where she was, the different odors in the air, even the two-tone claxon alert of an ambulance nearing its destination as the two women entered the hospital.

"But, how is Aunt Vangie now?" Alma asked.

"You can thank God she's much better. The car smashed into her right hip and broke it, and when she fell, she broke two of her ribs."

Alma winced.

"Don't worry. She's strapped up from her waist to her shoulder blades to help heal her ribs. And they operated on her broken hip. She's able to walk, but not too far and with a cane. She told me they're going to discharge her in another day or so."

Alma brightened. "It's a good thing I'm here. I can help her get around."

"Yes, I agree. But you know your aunt. She'll want to be independent," Claudine said. "They told her she might have a limp from now on, but that won't stop Vangie. She believes some people are attracted to a woman with a limp."

Claudine emitted a faint "humph" that began deep in her throat but remained captive in her closed mouth.

Quiet and looking from her left to her right, Alma walked in the kind of silence that keeps one company while wandering through the unknown.

"We're almost there. Her ward is near the top of this staircase." Claudine took a deep breath and began climbing the narrow steps. When they reached the end of their climb, she turned to the right and stopped abruptly in front of a set of doors.

"Here we are." With an exaggerated flourish of her arm, Claudine gestured that Alma should enter the room first.

Although most of the beds on both sides of the room had occupants, Alma had no difficulty finding her aunt. She was seated in a wheelchair, reading a book. Alma rushed to give and receive the hug-filled greeting she had expected to experience an hour ago.

"Aunt Vangie! How are you feeling?"

"Oh, my little Alma. I'm feeling so much better just seeing your smiling face."

Alma bent down and kissed Vangie's cheek.

"Looks like you found your way to Paris just fine, honey," Vangie said.

"And unlike you at present, your niece arrived in one piece," Claudine added.

Vangie looked at Claudine, then at Alma.

"Don't I have a good friend here, Alma?" she asked.

"I should say so. Claudine told me what happened and she brought me right here," Alma said.

Vangie winked at her friend.

"That's my Claudine," she said.

Alma looked over her shoulder and then at the nearby patients. She lowered her voice and bent over to be closer to her aunt.

"Is Claudine your special friend?" she asked.

"No, honey. Brickette's a special friend, but not the special friend you're asking about."

"Brickette?" Alma glanced at Claudine.

"That's the nickname Vangie gave me because of my red hair," Claudine said.

"Like I wrote in my letters to you, honey. There's lots of Negro Americans here in Paris," Vangie explained. "One of them is a woman who has the reddest hair I've ever seen. They call her Bricktop, or sometimes just Brick. Since Claudine's hair is red, but not quite as red as Bricktop's, I call her Brickette."

Claudine rolled her eyes, much to Alma's amusement.

"Bricktop has opened a jazz club with an after-hours room. She's been talking to me about working there for her," Vangie said.

Alma nodded. She knew better than to ask if working at night and coming home in the wee hours was safe. Just visualizing Aunt Vangie walking in the mostly deserted streets a few hours before dawn refocused Alma on Vangie's present state.

"Aunt Vangie, Claudine said you were run over by a car."

Vangie nodded.

"What happened with the driver? Did he stop? Was he drunk?"

"No. He didn't stop."

"So, he just hit you and kept going?"

"That's what happened, honey." Vangie shot a look at Claudine.

"And someone named Gérard saw the accident?" Alma asked. "Would Gérard recognize the driver or the car?"

"I doubt it, honey. It was too dark and it happened like that." Vangie snapped her fingers.

"Vangie says she doesn't know who was behind the steering wheel," Claudine said, "but she thinks she knows who was behind the so-called accident."

Alma looked at Claudine and then at Vangie.

"Who, Aunt Vangie?"

"Let's talk about all that later," Vangie said. She pointed at the white metal table next to her bed. "Hand me that picture, please. I want you to see someone who's very important to me."

Alma walked to the other side of the hospital bed and retrieved the picture. Without looking at it, she handed the photo to Vangie, who held it close to her chest.

"Alma, this is my special friend. She'd be right here to meet you if she weren't traveling in the States." Vangie caressed the picture's frame.

"She's an artist. She and her brother have gone to Chicago, Boston, and New York to meet with art gallery owners and some museum curators." Vangie paused. "With the accident and the operation on my hip, I've lost track of the dates. I thought for sure they'd be back by now."

Vangie held up the picture so Alma could see it more clearly.

Alma stared at the woman's portrait. She realized it was the same person whose photo she'd seen an hour ago while she waited for Claudine to return to the foyer in her aunt's flat. She recalled the feeling she'd had at that moment, the ephemeral half-memory of having seen that woman elsewhere. But when? Where?

The woman whose picture was here on the bedside table

was dressed more formally than she'd appeared in the first photograph. Her lowered eyes and delicate smile reflected a certain lack of self-assurance at most, or if not, an unconquered streak of shyness.

"What's her name, Aunt Vangie?"

"It's Elizabeth. Elizabeth Moune. Her family calls her Bette."

"She has a brother whose name is Hervé Moune," Claudine added.

Vangie reached for Alma's hand. "She and I are my third truth, Alma. Elizabeth and I love each other more than you can imagine."

Alma looked thoughtfully at Elizabeth Moune's photo.

"I know what you're thinking, Alma," Vangie said. "How could we love each other? She's white."

Alma shook her head. "I wasn't thinking that at all, Aunt Vangie."

"I never thought I'd fall in love with a white woman or that a white woman would fall in love with me. It's as if we love each other past our differences."

"Tell Alma about Hervé, Vangie," Claudine said.

Vangie inhaled deeply. "He's not thrilled that Elizabeth and I are seeing each other. In fact, Claudine thinks that's why he arranged the trip to the States, to separate us for a few weeks. But you know me, Alma. No man is going to stop me from doing whatever it is I want to do."

"Not even if he hires someone to run you over with a car?" Claudine asked.

"Oh, no! You think Elizabeth's brother planned your accident?" Alma asked.

Vangie glared at Claudine.

"I thought I asked you to keep that to yourself, big mouth."

"Alma deserves to hear everything," Claudine said softly.

Sensing Aunt Vangie's annoyance with Claudine and feeling overcome by her own exhaustion, Alma bent down and kissed her aunt's forehead.

"We're going to let you get some rest, Aunt Vangie. I promise I'll be back to see you tomorrow."

"All right, honey. You're probably tired from your trip. When you get back to my place, just make yourself to home."

Alma smiled. She'd always been amused when her aunt said "to" home, and not "at" home.

"I'm so glad you're here, Alma. Three years is a long time to go without seeing you."

"Don't worry about her, Vangie," Claudine said. "I'll make sure she's okay until you get out of here."

"*Merci, ma chère* Claudine. And, Alma, when we see each other tomorrow, you can tell me all about *your* three truths, or at least two of them." Vangie blew them kisses.

That evening, her first spent in Paris, Alma said nothing to Claudine about her two truths. She owed Aunt Vangie the privilege of being the first one to hear yes, she was a lesbian, and yes, she saw nothing wrong with that. Alma's third truth had yet to appear, if in fact it ever would. For now, she felt happier about her first and second truths than she did about the third one, the huge secret she might need to guard until she could no longer do so.

She had no idea how long she'd be able to remain silent about the woman her aunt loved so fiercely, a woman whose path Alma had crossed twice recently. How could she keep secret the evening she had answered curiosity's summons and risked reprimands by venturing up to the *SS Leviathan's* first-class promenade deck, only to be questioned by this woman's companion and insulted by virtue of her race and class? Why would she want to be silent about their frigid encounter in the train station in Cherbourg, especially if Vangie suspected Elizabeth's brother plotted the near-fatal car accident?

That first night in Paris, Alma lay in bed, too tired to go to sleep. She promised herself that she'd repay her Aunt Vangie's unwavering love and support by not telling her she'd come face-to-face with Elizabeth "Bette" Moune and her brother, Hervé. She knew Elizabeth was somewhere in Paris. If she were truly in love with Aunt Vangie, she would come to see her, and then, she'd see Alma as well.

Would Elizabeth own the race-tinged wound she'd

inflicted upon Alma when she used her complicit silence as a weapon? Would she feel bad and apologize? Would she question the depth of her love for Vangie, a love that is perhaps easier to express openly in Paris than it is in Philadelphia?

"We'll see if love has no color in Paris. We'll see," Alma murmured as she gave in to sleep.

DRIVING ALONE TO P-TOWN
IS NO EASY THING

Faith checked her appointment calendar to make sure she wasn't leaving anyone in a jam. Nope, everything was covered. The parent-school coalition workshops were set to begin on October first. Her staff of tutors could calm the September jitters the more zealous parents would begin experiencing by mid-month.

After one last glance at her schedule, and a momentary pang of guilt she felt when she thought about her kitty now on his own holiday at the pet spa, Faith was ready for the road. She put her suitcase and beach gear into the car's trunk, tapped her destination details into the navigation system, and adjusted the lumbar support of the driver's seat.

The notion that this trip was akin to running away or escaping an uncomfortable situation hadn't crossed her mind when she phoned her favorite bed and breakfast and requested a week-long reservation. After all, she deserved a vacation, and this time away would be her first getaway since she started her consultation business two years ago. It would also be the first vacation she spent all by herself.

Her friend Alicejane had accused her of being on the run, of avoiding the pitfalls and joys of traveling with a companion.

"Why drive all by yourself for eight long hours to a destination where you'll feel lonelier than you feel here? You're just running away, girl, and that won't solve your problem."

"I'm not running away," Faith said. "I'm just tired of things going wrong. After I broke up with Sarah, I was determined to stay single for a long time. I'd learned a lesson the hard way. Sarah was bed-hopping with every new woman who entered her sight line, and I never realized it until it was too late. Remember?"

Alicejane nodded.

"So, how could I have been stupid enough to make that same mistake twice?" Faith's voice rose in anger. "Kelly must have seen me coming."

"But you know P-town, Faith. You'll go for long walks on the beach and think about her. You'll stop in the bar, hear some sad song, and think about her. You'll see someone who reminds you of her, and you'll end up feeling hurt all over again."

"I don't think so. I've stopped missing her. And there's something healing about spending time with yourself and figuring out what happened, why it happened."

"Being alone means being lonely to me," Alicejane countered.

"Well, that's you. It's not me. And if I get tired of flying solo, maybe I'll have a wild fling."

"That doesn't sound like you, girl."

"Maybe it should be the new me. It's for damn sure Kelly isn't mourning our loss all by her lonesome."

"You don't know that for sure, Faith. I heard—"

"I don't care what you heard, Alicejane Cooper. What counts is where, and with whom, Kelly resumed spending her nights. We're done. I'm done."

Faith backed out of her driveway at four a.m. She figured an early departure would get her to P-town shortly after noon. The early morning traffic on the Pennsylvania Turnpike was light and the multi-lane New Jersey Turnpike wasn't much busier. For the first three hours, she listened to Philadelphia's talk radio station followed by one broadcast from New York City. Absorbed by the intelligent comments of a few callers and the stupidity of quite a few others, Faith let all thoughts of her business remain dormant. She did notice reckless truck drivers who sped past her and the occasional police car parked in full view on the side of the highway. On seeing the latter, she thought about Kelly and the comments she always made whenever they saw a cop who had commanded a driver to stop at the side of the road.

"Is the driver white or black?" she always asked.

If the driver were white, Kelly would utter, "No worries. He'll get a warning."

If the driver were a black male or female, Kelly would say, "Shit's gonna happen. They'll get a ticket plus moving violation points and be glad that's all."

Faith, ever cautious and filled-to-the-brim-with-survival-instincts, would allow an audible, "humph," but nothing more.

She steered her car onto an exit ramp that led to the last rest stop on the Garden State Parkway. She parked and entered the building. Passing the kiosks loaded with travel guides and maps, she headed to the restroom. With the exceptions of a toilet flushing noisily and a baby wailing angrily, the facility was quiet. It was still too early in the day for the rest stop to be busy.

Faith walked to the closest food and beverage vendor. With a cup of coffee in one hand and a sesame seed bagel in the other, she made her way back to her car. Perhaps it was the infusion of caffeine that propelled her eagerness to return to the road. When she considered the many miles and hours that stood between her and her destination, she felt empowered, not discouraged. She wondered why Alicejane was so certain that driving alone to P-town was no easy thing.

Of course, having shared the trip with Sarah once and with Kelly twice, Faith knew it was easier to drive in shifts, but driving solo wasn't an impossible feat. If she had the smarts and stamina to start a business all by herself, she could drive to Cape Cod alone. And if she could maneuver the rutted highway and narrow lanes of coastal Connecticut's portion of I-95, surely she'd continue growing her business. An idea coupled with the initiative to execute it properly led Faith to success, and one success led to others.

Faith recalled her concept to form a partnership with the South Philadelphia Health Collective, a sound idea professionally, but a foolish venture personally.

Faith crossed the room and extended her hand to the new arrival.

"You're Kelly Masters, aren't you?" she asked.

"Yes, I am."

"We were in high school together, the same class," Faith said, "but I don't remember seeing you at our reunion last year."

"I saw you there," Kelly said. "You're Faith Thomas, right? Or do you have a different last name?"

"No, it's still Thomas."

"So, what have you been doing all these years, Faith Thomas?"

"I've started my own consulting business. In fact, that's why I'm here tonight, to lead a workshop about assertiveness."

Kelly looked closely at the name tag pinned to Faith's jacket.

"Consult-and-Learn is your business?" she asked.

"Yes."

"That's very interesting."

Faith nodded.

Kelly said, "My colleagues and I at the Health Center arranged a series of workshops for our patients and their families. Your Assertiveness program is the first one on our schedule."

"Are you a physician?"

"Yes, I'm a pediatric endocrinologist."

"I don't think I've ever heard of that specialty," Faith said.

"Our group represents as many specialties as we can in order to cover as many community health needs as possible."

"That's wonderful. You're another academic success story from our alma mater," Faith said. "So, it's Doctor Masters."

"Yes, but it's still Kelly to a former classmate."

Kelly touched Faith's arm. "Listen, when tonight's workshop ends, we should talk about our plans for the rest of the series. There might be something more your company could contribute to us. There's a diner right across the street. Why don't we go there and compare notes?"

"Fine. I didn't have time for dinner, so coffee and something light sounds good to me."

****

Kelly Masters, usually a take-charge person, felt unsettled upon seeing Faith Thomas at the Health Center that evening. She remembered Faith. Acting on a friend's innuendo that she and Faith shared something in common was Kelly's sole motive for going to one more class reunion.

Halfway through that evening, she spotted Faith seated at one of the round banquet tables, examining photos another one of their classmates was shuffling like a deck of cards. As she watched, Kelly could see that Faith had not lost the persuasive smile and quiet manner she'd recalled from so many years ago. Kelly noticed also that instead of projecting the self-conscious girl she'd been years ago, Faith telegraphed self-assurance, a quality that Kelly found attractive, but at the same time a bit daunting.

Moments later, upon freeing herself from a conversation with two other attendees, Kelly looked once again for Faith. The chair she had occupied was now empty. Kelly scanned the room but found no trace of Faith. Since that evening one year ago, Kelly kept Faith's image tucked under the cover of her daily routines. The memory of Faith's smile emerged now and then between office appointments and hours spent with patients at the hospital.

The instant they spoke to each other at the Health Center and Kelly acknowledged her former classmate's direct gaze, she knew she'd made an error when she hadn't approached her at the reunion. The moment Kelly heard Faith's calm voice as she answered the workshop participants' questions, she knew she had to speak to this woman. The second Kelly imagined the gentleness of Faith's touch, she realized exactly why she'd never forgotten her.

****

Faith was tired of the constant conversation she heard from her car's radio and sampled various channels until she found one broadcasting Motown oldies. "Can I Get a Witness?" faded to "Shotgun," which morphed into "Since I Lost My Baby." All of those songs were the background music of her high school years, the years when Faith buried her attraction to girls, the years when she first became aware of Kelly and the undeniable need to stay away from even the slightest attempt to know her.

Kelly was that cool, unflappable, athletically coordinated, button-down-oxford-shirted, sure-of-herself young woman whom Faith needed to avoid lest she be tinged by the same rumors that followed Kelly throughout the halls of their school.

As Faith drove past the exit for Mystic, she recalled the phone call she made to Kelly from Mystic's Riverview Hotel. It was early in their relationship, and Faith recalled the regret she felt about having registered for a three-day seminar about entrepreneurship.

"Hello, Kelly. I'm glad I reached you at a free moment."

"Faith, I'm happy to hear your voice. How's the seminar going?"

"It's stimulating. I've thought of a few ideas for your future meetings at the Health Center."

"Oh, is that why you called me? I was hoping you wanted to tell me how much you enjoyed our dinner last week."

Faith thought she heard the slightest tease in Kelly's voice.

"I did enjoy the dinner, as well as your company."

"Glad to hear that. How long will you be in Connecticut?"

"I'll be back late morning on Thursday."

"Are you up for dinner on Thursday night? Barring any emergencies, I expect to be free about seven, and I'd like to hear all about your good ideas for the Health Center meetings."

"Is that why you want to have dinner with me?" Faith asked. "I hoped you'd say you'd enjoy spending more time with me."

Kelly laughed. "Touché," she said. "Why don't you

come to my place at seven-thirty?"

"I'll see you then."

"Travel safely, Faith."

Faith put her reverie on hold long enough to stop in Westerly, Rhode Island. She was hungry and she needed to stretch her legs. Seated at a picnic bench, she ate a tasteless sandwich and took sips from a bottle of water.

A family of three, two women and one child, claimed a nearby table. One of the women noticed Faith and offered a tentative smile. The child scowled and squirmed in an effort to turn her back to the women.

"Turn yourself around and eat your lunch," one of the women said.

"No. I don't like this food," the child screamed.

"Please eat something, honey," the tentative smile woman said.

Faith guessed the little girl was an expert at winning the "I'm-Going-To-Embarrass-The-Hell-Out-of-My-Over-Indul-gent-Under-Skilled-Parents-Until-I-Get-My-Way" gambit. In no time at all, she congratulated herself when the child's tenth blood-curdling scream was rewarded with an ice cream cone. A double dip.

Faith mused about the intelligence and manipulation skills of kids. They're so smart, yet so underestimated by most adults. Even the youngest of them who wins a duel of power versus power becomes a master fencer...fencer...

"Why are we fencing like this, Faith?" Kelly asked. "We've been seeing each other for months now, and it's obvious I care about you and you care for me. But now, when it seems we're getting close, you retreat and pull away from me. Why?"

"I don't know if I'm ready for anything more. After my last attempt at a relationship exploded in my face, I'm reluctant to jump into a new one."

"But, Faith, I'm not Sarah," Kelly protested. "I'm nothing like her.

Kelly reached out to Faith and pulled her within the borders of her arms. "It's not my intention to use and hurt you," she said. "You're special to me, and I want things to work between us."

Faith remained in Kelly's embrace. They gazed into each other's eyes until neither could continue breathing without sharing a deep kiss. Faith moaned and caressed Kelly's face softly with the back of her fingers.

With mutual and complete understanding, they undressed each other and lay down. Kelly began their liturgy of love with light-as-a-breath kisses she bestowed upon Faith's calves, then her knees, and to the insides of her thighs.

Faith grasped Kelly's shoulders and encouraged the deep kisses on her stomach and breasts. She called Kelly's name, softly at first, then louder and adamantly.

Gifted with the perception of all true lovers, Kelly knew when to slip into Faith and whisper, moan, and move her until they both rocked together and sang out their coming, joyfully.

Massachusetts began to whiz by. New Bedford, Lizzie Borden's Fall River, the signs for the Island Ferries, and the Bourne Bridge were the prelude to Route 6. Shortly after she drove past the Barnstable exit, rain began to fall, sporadically at first, then with more insistence. The noon traffic slowed to a crawl as a motorist struggled to steer his car to the side of the highway.

That poor driver, Faith thought. Who wants to have a car emergency in this crappy weather, an emergency…

"But you said you had an emergency, Kelly. That's why we couldn't get together tonight."

"I did have an emergency." Kelly couldn't hide her annoyance.

"It took all that time? The entire night?" Faith wouldn't back away from her interrogation.

"It takes time to bring a patient out of a sickle-cell crisis, especially when the patient is only six years old, in terrible pain, and too frightened to understand logic." Kelly's exhaustion sped her to a state of impatience. "You really don't understand the demands of my job, do you?"

"I do understand your job, and I admire the kind of doctor you are, how you care about your patients. What I don't understand in this case is how much you seem to care for this patient's mother, and why you felt you had to stay with her at the hospital all night."

Faith pressed her phone to her ear and heard Kelly exhale.

"Honey, I used to date Sheila, and I knew how upset she was about her son. I chose to stay with her at the hospital because that seemed like the right thing to do."

It was Faith's turn to inhale deeply and exhale slowly.

"Kelly, I need to know if there's a connection between Sheila and the last two evenings when you've been unavailable."

"Yes, there's a connection. May I explain?"

"No, I've already heard variations of what you're going to tell me. I'm not interested in hearing another story from a short-on-the-truth woman."

The exits for Dennis, Orleans, Brewster, and Wellfleet disappeared from her car's rearview mirror as, town by town, Faith made her way along the rain-filled highway. Well past the eighth hour of her journey, Faith's neck and shoulders felt stiff. Her back seemed molded to the driver's seat. Her eyes gritty from the forced concentration of staring at the windshield, Faith plodded past Truro and turned left onto Route 6A.

She passed North Truro's privately owned cottages and held her breath, as she always did upon approaching the road's last rise. There, spread out before her, was her reward, her first view of Provincetown. On a sunny day, the bay would sparkle as it met the spit of land that curved to embrace it. Today, the vista was gray, calm, and wet, but P-town ignored the weather and opened its arms like an old friend who wanted nothing more than to welcome her.

Bearing to the right onto Bradford Street, Faith drove the last half mile toward her lodging. She parked and checked in, grateful for the familiarity of the inn and of her favorite room. She showered, put on fresh clothes and a rain slicker, and decided to walk off the effects of driving for such a long time.

Three blocks into her hike brought her to the entrance of P-town's only women's bar. Faith side-stepped the rivulet of water running down the sloped entryway, and made her way inside.

Fewer than a dozen women were seated at the bar. Happy hour music defied the noisy gales that slapped rain against the glass doors that led to an outside deck.

Faith walked to a vacant barstool, sat down, and ordered a Bloody Mary. She looked at her image in the mirror behind the bar, held her drink aloft, and made the gesture of a celebratory toast.

"I don't know what the occasion is, but I'll join you in a second toast." A woman seated two stools away raised her glass and tipped it toward Faith.

"Thank you," Faith said.

"What's the special occasion you're celebrating, and why are you celebrating all by yourself?" the woman asked.

"Oh, just my safe arrival."

The woman pushed a folded advert toward Faith.

"I bet you didn't know there were lesbian whale-watching trips."

"Actually," Faith said. "I didn't realize there were lesbian whales."

The woman laughed the laugh of someone who'd spent too many hours sipping drinks without balancing the alcohol with food.

"Ever been on a whale watch?" the stranger asked.

"Yes, a few times. Lesbian, gay or bi, they're magnificent," Faith answered.

"How big is this boat, anyway?" The stranger pointed to the ad's photo of the Whale Watcher Too. "It doesn't look big enough to go ten miles out to sea."

"It's safe," Faith said.

"What if I get seasick?"

"If the weather's good and the water is calm, you shouldn't have to worry. You could always buy some Dramamine tablets or one of those seasickness-preventer wrist bands."

The stranger nodded and held up her empty glass.

"Have another Bloody Mary and keep my beer company. It's on me."

"No, thanks."

The woman continued to gaze at Faith. "Uh, are you

here waiting for someone?"

Faith paused, as if she were weighing the consequences of her answer.

"No."

The stranger moved one seat closer to Faith.

"Listen I heard these whale-watching trips are more fun if you go with a friend," she said. "My name is Sandy, and I'd like to be a friend of yours."

Despite her post-drive fatigue and the Bloody Mary she'd just downed, Faith was sure she didn't want to accompany this woman anywhere.

"Could I interest you in a tourist activity other than a whale watch, baby?"

Faith turned toward the voice she'd just heard.

Gazing back at her were Kelly's clear brown eyes.

Accusations, recriminations, and yes, joy moved through Faith's mind, but all that flowed from her mouth was a question followed by a short statement.

"Why did you go back to Sheila? I trusted you."

"You didn't trust me as much as you thought you did. If you had, you'd have given me a chance to explain."

Faith seemed to disregard Kelly's response.

"Why did you stay the night with her?"

"I stayed the night, but we certainly didn't sleep together. I've tried every way I know to contact you. I've left messages on your answering machine. I've sent you numerous texts that you've never responded to. The one day I did get to speak with you on your office phone, you were so cold to me. All business and nothing personal."

"My staff was nearby. What did you expect?"

"I expected you would have given me a chance to explain, or at least you would have agreed to see me so we could talk to each other."

"So now you show up here, trying to ruin my vacation?"

"I'm not here to ruin your vacation, Faith. I'm here because I need to see you."

Faith frowned.

"Alicejane told me where you'd gone."

"Oh, that's just great."

"Yeah, it is great. She cares a lot about you, about

us," Kelly said.

"I'm surprised you took the time to drive up here. Is Sheila back in your room wherever you're staying?"

Kelly couldn't suppress the faint smile Faith's question elicited.

"No. And I didn't drive. I flew to Boston and got a seat on the flimsy puddle jumper Cape Air calls an airplane."

Faith summoned a renewed hostility and stared at Kelly in anticipation of hearing a lie.

"Look, I have a friendship with Sheila. The notion of anything more is pure fiction," Kelly said. "You and I had so much to build on. We still do. And if you sit here right now and say that we don't, I'll be back at your door tomorrow. If you refuse me tomorrow, I'll return to you the day after that. I'm not going away, Faith. I'm not giving us up."

"And I'm not willing to make love with you one night and then find Sheila at your door the next night."

"That won't happen." Kelly touched her cheek. "I broke our date those two evenings because Sheila wanted me to check on her son, Skip. His pediatrician wasn't available, and I know Skip's treatment plan. He's never been a textbook patient. His sickling cycles are catastrophic."

Seconds passed silently as the two women looked at one another. "I want to believe you, Kelly."

"Please do believe me. I need to be with you. I love you."

Kelly pulled Faith close and Faith placed her arms on Kelly's shoulders. They looked at each other in silence for as much time as it took Faith's anger and hurt to begin falling away. Then they shared a kiss that felt like their first.

Faith eased herself from the barstool and slipped her hand into Kelly's. Excusing herself from the whale-watch enthusiast, Faith started for the door.

"Hey! I thought you weren't waiting for anyone," Sandy, the stranger, said.

"I guess I didn't realize I was," Faith said.

Two rain-drenched souls walked, arms entwined, back to the women's inn where they talked far into the night before loving away the memory of the long, lonely drive to P-town.

NOW

I never expected Carla would cross my threshold again. Not in this lifetime. Not after so many years, so many ruptured vows, and so many ragged memories.

I knew she was in town to do a reading and book-signing event and lead a writing workshop for university students. Although I hadn't planned to show up for the reading, I was curious about her. How different did she look now that the years have passed? Was the photo of her I saw in the   newspaper taken recently or some time ago? Was her hair as gray as mine? Had she put on weight like I have? I figured she'd still be beautiful. She'd still exude the emotional energy of a person who's never afraid to explore beyond her boundaries and always ready to share the results of her exploration.

I wondered what would happen if I did show up at the bookstore or attend her workshop? For the past few nights, I'd willed myself to sleep wrapped in the embrace of all the different scenarios that might unfold if I were to come face-to-face with Carla. I never reached the end of those imaginary episodes because they always faded into deep sleep. But the make-believe reunions found their way back to me each morning as I lay awake and then began my daily rituals. I couldn't stop recalling all that Carla and I had meant to each other, and I questioned who we were to each other today.

What a moot question. What a waste of time considering it.

What in the world would motivate Carla to see me? Maybe she'd want to dangle the glory of her success above my head. Perhaps she had the need to restoke the embers of the fury she felt when I left our relationship. Maybe she yearned to remind me of the sorrow and unbearable pain she suffered when I severed our union with the accuracy of a skilled surgeon timing and placing the first cut into her patient's flesh.

The more I dwelled upon Carla's possible reasons for seeing me, the more certain I was that she shouldn't.

That said, I listened half-a-dozen times to the message she'd left on my phone. She planned to arrive in Allerton two days before her book events were scheduled, and she thought it was time for her to see me. She didn't say it was time for us to see each other. She didn't ask if it were okay. She simply stated she'd see me around one o'clock this afternoon.

The hallway clock's Westminster chimes began their song as three knocks interrupted the peace outside my unlocked door.

"Come in." I tried to force strength and clarity from my throat.

Carla entered the narrow foyer and stood still, as if she were deciding at the last second how best to greet me. She moved forward, walking in her Carla-kind-of-way, with purposeful determination. Her eyes telegraphed wariness. Her lips ceded to a tentative smile.

"Hello, March," she said.

Unable to believe the reality of her presence, I nodded my greeting instead of speaking it.

I know this sounds strange, but the second Carla spoke my name I heard all the "hello March's" she'd ever said to me. Every single breathy, filled-with-trust-and-love greeting she'd ever uttered.

In that second, all I could think of were the lyrics of Bill Withers's "Hello, Like Before." I knew I couldn't sing the words, and I was damn sure Carla wouldn't appreciate the gesture. So instead, I concentrated on how gracefully she wore her age. The creases that punctuated her smiles were deeper than I recalled, and now shallow lines travelled from east to west across her forehead. Here and there her hair's silver strands twisted themselves amiably into curls that were still dark brown for the most part.

"How are you, March?"

"Okay," I mumbled then said louder, "I'm okay."

I wanted, no, I needed to assure both of us that I was fine.

I looked into Carla's eyes, in search of her feelings or, at least, her thoughts. All I found was the familiar gentle gaze of her kindness. I saw no trace of anger or recrimination.

"I had trouble finding you, so I'm glad you still have the same phone number," Carla said. "How long have you been here?"

"Only a week," I answered.

Carla pointed to a nearby chair.

"May I sit down?" she asked.

Sure. Be my guest."

"Being your guest feels so strange, especially after all this time."

I nodded and watched Carla watching me. Should I offer her a cup of coffee or tea? Should I tell her how strange I felt being here, that it wasn't exactly my choice, just the lesser of two evils?

"Do you miss your house?"

"Yes, I do."

Truth be told, I missed just about everything that once defined my existence, things I'd thrown into the wind during careless hours filled with wants I hadn't been able to identify.

"Would you like something to drink, coffee or tea?" I asked.

Carla shook her head. "No, thanks. It's been such a long time, and I wanted to stop in to see you." She paused. "You know. To see how you're doing."

"That's very kind of you. I know you have a busy schedule."

Carla frowned. "I really needed as much as wanted to see you."

I couldn't respond. I couldn't find the words to thank her for not being haughty, for being gracious and kind and not lording it over me that right wins out in the end. No, that's not true. I did have the words. I've always had the words. I just couldn't force them to overtake my pride and express themselves. In that moment, thanking Carla Jensen for being kind and compassionate was my insurmountable challenge.

Carla stood. She moved toward me and extended her right hand.

As I raised my left hand to hold hers, I saw sorrow wash over her face. I'd imagined this moment could arrive, and I'd dreaded it. I knew Carla's heart, and I knew she wouldn't be able to staunch the pity she felt for me, for us. Despite seconds of silence, she communicated the feelings of every woman who's continued to care about a perfidious lover.

I'd known for a long time that witnessing Carla's pity would reduce my pride even more than I'd reduced it myself.

"I'd like to see you again this week while I'm here," she said.

I shook my head. "No, not a good plan."

"Are you sure about that?"

I nodded.

Carla turned toward the foyer.

"Thanks for the visit," I said.

"Good-bye, March."

I watched her open the door and disappear as it closed behind her. A scant second later I heard her voice utter a question. Bits and pieces of its answer crept under my door like an odorless, invisible gas.

"Ischemic stroke, left side…good effort with PT…walking better…speech almost fully recovered…another week or two…return home with help."

I'd heard all of those answers before, when I'd been the one asking the questions. And yes, I was going home just as soon as I could take command of my mind and body. As much as I wanted to return home, I knew I wouldn't be going back to a home filled with love and tenderness.

Carla would never be there. She had uttered her final "Good-bye, March."

Filled with the same regret I'd felt when I dismissed Carla from my life, I made my way slowly to the door to make sure it was closed. I didn't want anyone to witness the tears coursing down my face as I tried in vain to stifle my sobs.

HOW IT BEGAN

I always felt I'd know the woman I'd love forever as soon as I saw her. I couldn't have described her beforehand because her image was obscured and hazy somewhere in my subconscious, below the daily tedium of people who passed by me and tucked under bits of conversation I heard and made in the course of every day. Had anyone pressed me to describe this woman's appearance, 1 couldn't have done it.

Now that I've seen and spoken to her, I realize I'm drawn to more than a person's physical traits. I'm attracted to her curiosity, her desire to understand as much as possible, her empathy, and the sincerity with which she asks questions and offers her own opinions.

I first noticed her three Sundays ago.

She walked slowly past our table in the bookstore and disappeared behind the contemporary fiction shelves. After a while she reappeared. With book in hand, she sat on one of those huge armchairs the bookstore staff placed here and there for customers who forget they're in a store, not in a public library. For the past three Sundays, she's claimed the same chair, the one that gave her an unobstructed view of our small group. If she'd wanted to, she could have drawn a straight line between the front of her chair and the less comfy one I occupied. If she'd been able to read our lips, she could have participated in our discussions.

When I watched this woman sit in the same place two Sundays in a row, I had to admit I thought it was strange. Why was she so interested in observing us? I watched her watching us as we took turns reading and writing quickly in our notebooks. It must have been obvious that we gathered each week to do more than socialize.

The notebook covers revealed who we were, or at least how we wished others to perceive us. Hand-tooled leather, tattered-edge cardboard, small spiral-bound, full-size spiral-bound, unbound sheets of paper, cover photo of the Eiffel Tower, and back-cover picture of Josephine Baker introduced us to anyone who was interested.

Back then, did we realize we wanted to be noticed or perhaps to represent something that contradicted the daily stream of negative stereotypes placed upon our shoulders? Did we see our bi-weekly meetings as attempts to clear the fog of misrepresentation that hung low over many of us, educated or not? Did we believe the degrees we bore would shield us like suits of armor? And how did we react when we realized the degrees were no more than sheets of paper that sometimes made us less than trustworthy in the eyes of our contemporaries?

I doubt it. We were too enmeshed in our desire for a place at the table, the one where the literati sat. So, we met once a week to share rejection notes, announcements of writing contests, calls for submissions, and reworded pages of our works-in-progress.

Although it wasn't easy to put aside our individual ambition long enough to accommodate the zeal of others, we struggled through the process. We found comfort and reassurance because of our common ambition, and we trusted one another.

If our group of writer wannabe's invited curious glances, the glances were short lived and not at all memorable. That's why this woman's presence, albeit at a distance but for the third consecutive Sunday, was odd.

I wasn't the only one who'd seen her watch us.

"Looks like our mystery woman is back," Carlos said. "I think she's interested in you, March."

"I doubt it," I said.

That very thought had crossed my mind once, okay twice. The second time it got stuck in my vanity, but since I'd never seen the woman smile directly at me, I'd begun to conclude she was some kind of nut. My fiction-churning imagination conjured scenes in which she was stalking me. That's when I knew I was getting carried away.

"You could test my theory, March. Flash one of your famous smiles and see if she smiles back," Carlos said.

Instead of smiling, I pouted.

"Go on. I dare you," he persisted.

"I'd rather smile at Joie since it's her turn to read."

I looked away from Carlos and turned toward Joie who picked up her short pile of papers.

"Okay," she said. "This is the beginning of the first chapter of my new work."

As Joie began to read, the stranger got up from her chair and walked toward us. Joie reached the end of a sentence just as the woman stopped a foot away from our table.

"May I join you?" she asked.

Six pairs of eyes looked at her.

Joie pointed to the empty chair directly across from me.

"Sure. It's a free country," she said.

"Well," the woman said, "not always and not everywhere."

"You can say that again." Carlos stroked his beard-covered chin. "I'm Carlos, by the way."

"And I'm Carla."

Clearly amused by the similarities of their names, the woman tilted her head and offered Carlos the faintest wave.

One by one we spoke our names.

"Dana, Richard, Alyse, Joie, March."

The new arrival looked at me.

"March? Are you named after the family in Alcott's 'Little Women'?" she asked.

"No, I'm not." I hesitated and then added, "My mother's name was April. She said from the day I was born she wanted to put me before her."

"What a tender gesture."

The woman smiled and held my gaze in hers for what seemed like a full minute.

I've held women in my gaze as many times as I've been held in theirs, and I've been held by gentle arms and strong legs eager to impress their desire upon me. I've been held aloft by the faith and light emanating from others' hopes. I've also been held in abeyance by women waiting for someone better to come along. I've been held accountable for the quick visits I've indulged in to quell the restlessness that accompanied my temporary boredom. But I swear, I've never been held captive by eyes quite like those holding onto me now.

If I'd had the sense I was born with, I would have raised my arms above my head and surrendered everything to the custody of those translucent, brownish-green eyes right then and there.

"Are you a book-discussion group?" she asked us.

"Once in a while," Carlos said. "But we're really a writer's group. We share our work with each other and ask for feedback."

"And we bend over backwards to keep our comments kind and constructive," Alyse added.

I nodded toward Joie.

"Joie was in the middle of her reading. We should let her continue," I said.

Carla pressed her lips together and leaned forward. "I'm so sorry I interrupted you."

"No problem." Joie focused on the paper in front of her.

A half hour later we stood up to leave. We'd supported Joie's work, given her some suggestions, and agreed we'd meet in two weeks.

"Do you think you'll join us again?" Carlos asked our newcomer.

"I'd really enjoy that, if it's okay with everyone." Carla looked at each of us, as if she were asking our permission.

Did she really think we'd say no?

Dana, who'd been her usual quiet self, stared at Carla. "You do know we're all queer, don't you?"

"Everyone's queer in some way or another, right?" Carla answered.

Carlos tweaked his beard and cleared his throat. "But we're especially queer, my dear. As in lesbian, gay, bisexual, and trans."

"That's what I'd been hoping," Carla said. "I wasn't sure at first, and it took me a couple of weeks before I figured I could trust my instincts."

A bloom of satisfaction flowered in my chest. "So, it's settled. See everybody in two weeks," I said.

I turned around to walk toward the bookstore's exit and found Alyse keeping in step with me. We left the store's warmth and stood in the cold near the parking lot.

"Well." Alyse took a deep breath, more in anticipation

of what she was about to say than in response to the icy air. "Now we have to change the name of our group."

"Why?"

"Because 'Queer Literati of Color' no longer fits us. It's not accurate if the newbie has joined our group."

"But she's as queer as we are," I protested.

"That's true, March. But she's not exactly a person of color," Alyse said. "You did notice that, didn't you?"

"Oh, yeah," I said.

But in truth, all I'd noticed about Carla that day was her smile and her eyes. In the years that followed, I grew to second-guess her curiosity, to appreciate her desire to understand absolutely everything and to be understood absolutely. We became as close to each other as skin is to bone.

During the course of those years, I learned to understand some things that are basic but go unnoticed. I figured out why Carla's strides are planted heavily, noisily, while mine are soft and barely leave a footprint. I came to understand why Carla always walks to the front row of an auditorium while I gravitate toward the middle. I got why Carla can propel herself to the beginning of lines while I linger back.

Somewhere along the way, I forgot that beneath the differences imposed by the rest of the world lay our sameness, and I cracked under the pressure of that lost memory. The crack fissured and became an ugly, jagged thing that sent us in different directions away from each other.

Years would pass before we'd search for a way back.

EPILOGUE

"Ms. March?"

I looked toward the source of the voice and saw Ayesha, the young CNA who has helped me from time to time during my stay here in Rehab.

"Good morning, Ayesha."

"This is your big day, Ms. March."

"Yes, it is. And I'm glad you stopped by. I want to thank you for everything you've done to help me get back on my feet."

"You did all the work." Ayesha looked away from me shyly before she continued. "Ms. March, I want to thank you for encouraging me to go back to school, even if it's only part time and at night."

I touched her arm. "It looks like we've helped each other, doesn't it?"

"Yeah, I guess we have. Oh! I'm supposed to tell you your transport person will be here in an hour."

"Thanks, hon. And remember to keep taking good care of your little boy. He's your most important job."

"I will, Ms. March."

I watched Ayesha retreat, and I recalled the conversations we'd had about her son and about children in general. I told her how much my partner had wanted us to have children and how much I'd stood in the way. Back then, there weren't any state or federal laws to protect Carla and me. Either she would have been the legal parent or I would have. We couldn't *both* be the official parents with joint custody rights. We'd talked about adopting a biracial child, although I understood the barriers that faced black and mixed-race children. Carla had a clue, but not much more than that.

We debated the issue any time our relationship was devoid of other problems. I remember arguing about the pros and cons of having a family those times when our union teetered on the perilous precipice of being okay or not okay.

Ayesha's exit became another's entrance.

"May I come in?"

Mary O'Connor, my Patient Assistance Navigator, walked into the room and gestured for us to sit down. She sat across from me and leaned forward, a posture she assumed every time we talked.

"I imagine you're feeling happy about going home today, March."

"You don't know the half of it, Mary."

Mary tilted her head and smiled a smile I might have labeled false or at least practiced, had I not spoken to her frequently during my stay here.

My infallible sixth sense assured me Mary's smile was genuine. Over the course of the last three weeks, her gently asked, thoughtful questions convinced me that she cared about my physical progress as well as my ability to take care of myself after leaving the rehab facility and returning to my home. To be honest, a few of our discussions led me to think Mary's concern went beyond how well I could handle cooking, showering, shopping, and going from point A to point B.

A few days after Carla's unexpected visit, Mary sat down with me, showed me my therapists' charts, and told me I'd begun to reverse the progress I'd made.

"I'm concerned about you, March," she said. "See the graph on this chart? These two lines reflect your daily physical-and occupational-therapy results. They're supposed to be going upward, not downward."

I stared at the blue-and-green lines' trajectories and recalled the names of two of my elementary school teachers, the two who taught me and my classmates how to read charts and graphs. It was easier for me to deal with those memories than to explain why I began to spiral downward.

"Do you want to talk about what's going on?"

Mary sounded more like a counselor than someone whose job it was to coordinate my rehab regimen and organize my post-rehab details.

"I stopped pushing myself," I said.

Mary nodded and seemed to agree with my response. "Do you know why you stopped pushing yourself?"

The old me would have stonewalled, but the newer me, the post-stroke-fix-it-now-or-never me obeyed my urge to share a confession with her.

"I've been feeling depressed, and I'm smart enough to recognize it."

"Some depression is natural following a stroke. In your case, you didn't experience it right away. In your rush to get better and recover what you'd lost physically, you might have ignored any emotional issues that stood in your way." Mary paused. "A delayed reaction is natural also," she added.

Mary looked at me as if she expected I was going to say more. When I retreated to silence, she spoke again. "I was wondering if there was a connection between the onset of your sad feelings and the visitor who was here that first weekend."

"Possibly. No, probably," I said.

"The nurse on duty that afternoon made a note in your chart. She wrote that she heard you crying shortly after your visitor left."

"Well, there's nothing wrong with the nurse's hearing, is there?" I said.

Mary laughed. "No, there isn't."

My instinct to deflect painful, unpleasant incidents and reroute them toward anything humorous never failed me.

"By the way, March, there's nothing wrong with crying."

Apparently, Mary's ability to recognize using humor to skirt around something serious hadn't failed her. "Would it help if you could talk about the reasons for your tears?"

"No doubt it would, Mary. But here's the problem. I've never been able or willing to talk about why I pushed my partner away. Not then, nor during all of these years since we parted ways."

"Maybe it's not too late. Especially if your crying means you still have feelings for her."

Mary flipped through the pages of my therapy records and held up a different graph. "From the day you arrived here, your strongest ability has been your speech."

I touched the red line inscribed on the graph. Over the span of twenty sessions, its path consistently moved upward.

"Look, you kept improving, even when your PT and OT progress slowed down." Mary held the first graph next to the second one. Then she handed me the binder that contained all of my information. "Read the note your speech therapist wrote on February eleventh, the middle of your second week here."

I turned a few pages until I saw the one with the date Mary singled out, and I began reading aloud.

"March's voice continues to strengthen. She is more animated and emotive today. She initiates conversation and produces descriptive vocabulary as well as longer, more complex sentences, both declarative and interrogative. The connection of thought, memory, emotion, and spoken language is increased. Creative expression is returning."

"Wow!" I said then added, "I guess 'Wow' isn't the best example of a complex sentence, but it does demonstrate the connection of thought, emotion, and language."

Mary laughed. "I'm not a doctor, March, but I believe in time you'll be able to write another novel."

An entire novel? I didn't know if I'd ever write another one.

"I also believe you can talk about the issues that caused you and your partner to grow apart," Mary said.

"I'm not so sure, about that," I answered. "Too many years have passed. Too much silence has wedged itself between us. But thanks for the good thoughts. You've gone above and beyond the responsibilities of a Patient Assistance Navigator."

"Oh, you're welcome." Mary fidgeted. "And you're right. I'm supposed to have boundaries. Right now, I need to help you have a smooth discharge, right?"

"Right." I hoped my saying "above and beyond" hadn't hurt Mary's feelings, but I needed to reel in her questions and reset her compass. Any notions she might have about my relationship with Carla were best kept to herself. I'd stopped having those notions a long time ago, and I assumed

Carla had banished them as well.

Mary cleared her throat. "For the first week, you'll receive two wellness phone calls per day, one in the morning and the other after noon. Sometime this afternoon you'll get a phone call from the in-home therapy agency. They want to set up your schedule."

I nodded. "I had time to do some online research. That agency has a good reputation."

"Yes, that's true. Of course, your home therapy sessions will differ from your sessions here."

"Understood," I said. "For one thing, I don't have a therapy studio in my house."

"Right. You have a follow-up appointment with your doctor two weeks from today. Do you have any questions?"

"Just one. Have you arranged for someone to prepare breakfast, lunch, and dinner for me?"

Mary chuckled. "No. Your OT therapist signed off on your ability to fend for yourself in the kitchen, so I'm afraid the catered meals have ended."

"Catered? Seriously?"

We both laughed at the idea of comparing the rehab's three meals a day plus an evening snack to a caterer's service.

I let a sigh escape and admitted silently that laughter had been missing from my life for a long time. I'd begun to relearn its sound the day after I'd seen Carla and allowed myself to cry about us. Since then, I'd been laughing about several things, like my missteps, my inability to finish the last two manuscripts I'd tried to complete, and the Swiss-Cheese-like holes in some of my memories.

"Ms. O'Connor, Ms. March's transport is here." Ayesha stood at my doorway.

"Well, this is it, March." Mary extended her arm.

I brushed it aside and hugged her.

"If you need anything, I'm as close as your phone."

"Maybe we could meet for lunch sometime," I said. "You could ask me a few of your probing questions and therapize me for the price of your meal."

"Maybe we can do that." Mary gave me her thoughtful smile. Her lips spread slowly, as if they were trying to decide exactly how pleased they were. "Take it easy in the beginning, and increase your activities day by day."

I planned to do just that. I imagined doing everything I'd always done, albeit a bit more slowly. I visualized returning to my routine and spending my time as I wished. I was used to listening to my own voice answer my own questions. Not to mention fighting the occasional temptation to contact Carla. Thoughts of her would float through my mind from time to time, but when those thoughts made their appearance, I figured it wouldn't do either of us any good to drag out the bad memories. Anyhow, I was accustomed to being without her, and I assumed being without me suited her fine. That's why seeing her here was such a surprise, a bittersweet one.

"Everything's out of the closet and drawers, right?" Mary asked.

"Yes."

I took a final look at the room that had been my home for the past four weeks.

"Would you like me to walk with you to the exit?" Mary asked.

"Thanks, but I think I'd like to make the trip unassisted."

I entered the hallway and looked to the left, then the right, hoping to see Ayesha one last time. Instead, I saw a different staff member carrying my suitcase and walking toward the building's entrance.

As we got closer to the reception desk, I noticed how bright everything looked with the late-morning sun streaming through the door's glass sidelights.

The staffer waited for me to join him at the entrance before he opened the door. We walked out into the day, and he pointed at a car parked at the curb, its hazard lights blinking.

"There's your transport, ma'am," he said.

I imagine he walked to the car and put my suitcase in the trunk, but I swear I didn't see him do that. Nor do I recall thanking him. All I saw was Carla, standing beside the car, waving at me.

I stood erect and made every effort to move toward her

just as I had years ago. Without a single trace of happiness missing from my smile, I waved hello and called her name.

"I hope it's okay, March. I thought I could drive you home."

"It's perfectly okay. I'm glad to see you."

I sat down in the passenger's seat and watched as she slid behind the steering wheel and looked over at me before she started the engine.

"I hope we make some time to talk," she said. "It doesn't have to be today, but there's a lot I need to tell you."

"We'll make the time. There's a lot I need to hear."

"Good." Carla steered her car away from the curb.

"For a while," I said, "I may not be able to walk quickly, but I sure can talk up a storm. Most importantly, I know how to listen. I don't think I had that skill years ago."

Carla touched my arm. "Neither of us knew how to listen." She smiled, more with her brownish-green eyes than with her lips

And I gave myself to those eyes. Those eyes that had entered my soul long ago. Those eyes that held a promise to trust and hold us close to each other once again.

AFTER SHE LEFT

Suzanne backed into the parking space just as the train eased away from the station. It didn't matter if she arrived in time for that particular train or for the next one. In the afternoon, the trains came and went every twenty minutes or so, and she had more than enough time to reach today's destination.

She'd been aiming to take the three-thirty-seven train when, just two miles short of the station, one of those sunset-yellow-and-black school buses derailed her plans by inserting itself right in front of her car. The bus chugged along, stopping every three hundred yards to expel a gaggle of school kids.

Gangly, pre-adolescent boys launched themselves helter-skelter from the vehicle's steps while their more graceful female schoolmates stepped their way carefully from the bus to the street.

Corner after corner, Suzanne watched different boys run, drag their bookbags as they zigzagged over the wide sidewalks, and playfully punch each other as they raced to put distance between themselves and the bus stop. She noticed most of the girls walked in twos or threes. A few singletons asserted their lack of need for companionship and faded unobtrusively into artfully designed landscapes or behind the doors of Tudor-inspired houses.

Although they didn't make physical contact with each other the way the boys did, the girls exchanged smiles and shared conversations. Their smiles suggested connections far more intimate than the jabs their male counterparts traded. Surely some of their giggles sealed secrets they would treasure for as long as they could hold on to their fragile pre-pubescent friendships.

Right now, they assume their friendships will last forever, Suzanne thought. They take it for granted that the ribbons binding their relationship will endure. Forever friendships are a given, right? No, they're not. They're never guaranteed.

Permanence hadn't been certain for her and Michelle, and Suzanne knew it wouldn't be a lock for these girls either.

A thick, heavy fog settled over Suzanne anytime she recalled the moments of losing her feelings of awkwardness with Michelle and sharing her secrets, even the frightening ones, with her.

Suzanne followed the school bus as it ascended a hill and stopped to expel more kids. Once it began moving forward again, Suzanne looked beyond it and saw the entrance to the train station. She squinted as the blinking lights of the railway traffic barrier descended slowly to block cars on either side of the road from crossing the railroad tracks. She knew the slow pace she'd driven behind the school bus would cause her to miss yet another train. No matter.

Once again, the bus's crimson stop signals pulsed rhythmically and a pair of feet hit the ground. As the solitary student crossed the street, he glanced over his shoulder and nodded at the bus driver.

Suzanne watched the boy and wondered if the bus driver had returned the nod. She noticed the boy's jacket was zipped closed from bottom to top. The straps of his bookbag were looped securely around his shoulders.

He's a loner, she thought. An only child, a rule follower, an outcast plugging through his school days in stoic silence. He's probably one of the few black students who attend his school. After all, there aren't that many black people who live in this area. No doubt he gets good grades, and he'll go to an HBCU where he'll do exceedingly well in academics but embarrassingly poorly in the social arts. He won't know how to be comfortable in his own skin when, for the first time, his skin matches that of the other students.

Suzanne had that boy's future plotted before he reached the other side of the road. That's the kind of thing Suzanne did. She observed people constantly. She filled in their backstories. She overheard their conversations and silently resolved their problems. Solving other people's problems fired her brain synapses during those moments when thinking about her own path through life was too difficult for her to do.

The entire time she was in the hospital she devoured the empty hours by spinning narratives about every doctor, nurse, technician, and transport person with whom she came in contact. When Michelle's visits dwindled from every day to only a few minutes every other day, and then to a quick phone call twice a week, Suzanne seized upon imagining the ins and outs of other people's lives. Composing others' biographical fictions became her parachute to a safe landing.

Fifteen minutes before the next train's arrival, Suzanne steered her car into the station's small parking lot. She stayed in her car and stared at a wooden shelter near the tracks. How old and decrepit, she thought.

As a car parked next to hers, Suzanne looked at its female driver. She found it remarkable that in the last thirty minutes, she'd seen two other black people, the schoolboy and now this woman. Counting herself, that made at least three people of color living out here where most of the population was white. How many times had she and Michelle speculated the earth had opened up and swallowed all the other black folks who inhabited this tiny section of the world?

While the speculation of that having happened angered Michelle, it made Suzanne thoughtful.

"Why do you get mad when someone calls you a dyke, but not when someone treats you differently because you're black?" Michelle had asked her that question several times when she couldn't find any other reason to instigate an argument.

"Because I can't be mad twenty-four seven. Why should I drive my blood pressure through the roof and shorten my life?"

Suzanne watched the newcomer open her car's door and exit the vehicle.

The woman was built as solidly as an Edmonia Lewis statue. She stood next to her car, feet planted firmly on the ground, noiselessly conveying a don't-fuck-with-me attitude. She turned slightly and looked toward Suzanne.

The two women exchanged smiles and nodded at each other.

Immediately, Suzanne conjured a conversation she might have had with the woman if they'd known each other.

"Are you okay? Is everything all right?" the woman would ask.

"Everything's fine now, thank you," Suzanne would answer." I made my decision some time ago. Now I just have to follow through."

"I understand your pain," the woman would say. "And I believe you're doing the right thing."

The woman would turn away and continue to wait for the next train's arrival.

Their imaginary conversation ended, and Suzanne squinted at a pin-point of light wavering in the distance. The beam grew larger and brighter with each passing second. Suzanne remained seated in her car. What did it matter if she failed to get on this train? She had time to wait for the next one.

She watched as one-by-one this incoming train's passengers stepped down onto the platform.

The woman with whom she'd had a fantasy conversation moved from her spot next to her car and walked against the tide of pedestrians. She reached out and embraced one of the female passengers.

Suzanne saw the two women exchange smiles and share a kiss. She breathed deeply and sighed. Years earlier she and Michelle would have greeted each other exactly as these two women had. But now, her sigh went unheard just as her pleas had fallen on ears that refused to listen.

Suzanne got out of her car and removed an envelope from her handbag. She placed it face up on the dashboard, as if it were one of those parking receipts belched up by a municipal parking authority kiosk. Then she tucked her bag out of view under the driver's seat, hugged her jacket close to her body, and began walking.

When she reached the end of the macadam platform, she kept walking. She slowed her pace in order to navigate the weeds and trash that marked the end of the train station's property. The thistle's whip-like stems reached out and left scratches on her legs. She ignored the painful pricks, and she refused to look down at the network of red scratches now etched upon her legs.

She knew this territory and where its overgrown, trashy stretch would come to an end. Just a bit farther, and the rails would lose the company of soil, trees, and weeds. Four-foot-high cement walls built on both sides of an overpass supplanted Nature and stood guard over the road below.

That place was Suzanne's destination. That's where she planned to exercise her free will, either by scaling the low barrier and leaping down onto the busy roadway below, or by inserting herself between the side of the speedy train and the cement wall. No matter which method she chose, she would be assured of a quick exit from life.

Suzanne felt a vibration as she walked close to the tracks. The trembling began under the soles of her feet and traveled up through her legs and into her chest. She turned around and saw the train's bright headlight cut through the late-day gloom and illuminate her path to the biggest decision she'd ever have to make. She had only seconds to decide her ending. Mere seconds to do the act many thought cowardly, but she considered an act of brave self-determination.

The train's thunderous roar filled her ears as Suzanne pressed her back against the rough cement wall. Warm air assaulted the side of her body that would feel the train's impact first. She closed her eyes and forgave everyone who ever hurt her. Everyone except Michelle.

Suzanne opened her eyes the second she heard the train, an express headed to the city, speed by the station without stopping, or for that matter without slowing. She tapped her steering wheel and looked at her watch.

It was six-thirty and the parking lot was almost empty.

Most of the commuters are in their homes now, she thought. Some are eating dinner with their families who aren't listening to each other describe their daily stresses. Some are stuck in their own minds, already sleepwalking through the next day's drive to the train station, to the coma-inducing ride into town followed by the humdrum walk to their office.

As she stared into the darkness, Suzanne tried to remember when she'd first begun her tale-spinning habit, a practice that came to devour hours upon hours of her days. When had her imagination begun veering toward death and then to her own demise?

Struggling to put her memories in order, she pushed her car's ignition button. She'd always made up fictions about other people, even when she was a little girl. She rationalized it was what children who don't have siblings do to fill up empty rooms and create companions. And she recalled exactly when she began composing fantasies about dying. It was the morning of Michelle's departure. Since then, Suzanne's imaginary plays had become one-act-only dramas. These dramas all ended the same way. As of today, Suzanne realized she'd created far more than an imaginary tale. She'd created a plan.

She backed out of the parking space and steered the car toward the parking lot's exit. She glanced at her reflection in the rearview mirror and smiled.

"It's a good plan," she said aloud. "One that will work when I come back here tomorrow."

A NIGHT BEYOND THE CITY LIMITS

"Where the heck are we headed?" I asked Marie.

I'd been hesitant to take this trek, but my friend kept harping on me about the funk I'd been in since I'd broken up with Terez.

"You need to get out and enjoy yourself," Marie preached over and over again.

Now it felt like we'd been in Marie's car for hours. We drove on busy four-lane highways, passed by shopping strips, a large mall, a movie theater complex, and at least two different entrances to the interstate. Acres of brightly lit commercial spaces yielded to ribbons of residential areas. Houses, mostly medium sized with front lawns and deep porches that suggested shared beers with neighbors eager to trade gossip, lined our trail to a destination I'd heard of but never visited.

"Tell me again why we're heading so far away from the city to buy a drink and gawk at women we don't know," I said. "Are there any women of color out here?"

I knew the absence of black women wouldn't bother Marie. Two of her former girlfriends were white. A third one was Asian.

Marie squinted at the road ahead of us. "Hold on. I don't want to miss the turn. It's around here somewhere." She tightened her grip on the steering wheel.

"Here it is," she said. "Now, just three-quarters of a mile to go."

I gritted my teeth. An all-consuming darkness surrounded us. A setting like this one used to awaken my curiosity. Now, post Sandra Bland and so many others, the isolation warned me to be on the lookout for police cars with flashing red lights. My belief that there were places where people simply accepted each other peacefully had been shattered by cameras whose lenses bore witness to the hatred rooted in generations-old fear.

"Marie, you've driven us to the middle of who knows where. There aren't even street lights out here."

Marie laughed. "Don't worry, Jaie," she said. "I guarantee you'll have a good time."

"How many times have you been to this bar anyway?"

"Two."

I shook my head. "Why did I let you talk me into this?"

"Probably because you're tired of sitting at home alone on a Saturday night."

"Not really. And if I were, I could always go to Señora's or The Q Spot."

"The Q Spot?" Marie asked. "Not now. We vowed to never spend another dime in that place. You can go back there if you want to, sister, but I won't."

In my trepidation about tonight's activity, I'd forgotten about the newspaper articles and soundbites recorded when the Q Spot's owner was questioned about his patron quota policies. My memories of the protest demonstrations that followed the bar's publicity had temporarily vanished, like so many other details surrounding the end of my relationship with Terez.

"I'll go to Señora's because it's the only women's bar left in town, but I won't step inside The Q Spot." The tone of Marie's voice was laden with finality.

We approached a sharp *Y* intersection, and Marie steered her car to the right. Fifty yards or so beyond that turn was an unpaved expanse of land. A one-story building stood at the far end of the rut-filled area.

"We're here." Marie aligned her car with other ones.

I looked through the windshield at the unadorned building that faced us. "I'm not impressed."

Although the bright floodlights affixed to the building's eaves illuminated a path, the structure's painted white bricks, steep cinder-block steps, and decrepit Lodge No. 42 sign suspended above the entrance were jarring, not welcoming.

"You have to admit parking here is better than driving to the rooftop of that vomit-and urine-infested lot down the street from Senora's."

Although we were far from the city, simply recalling the odors that lined both sides of the alley leading to Señora's forced me to hold my breath for a second longer than necessary. I exhaled and noticed a thin trail of my breath rise in front of my eyes. I inhaled once more and felt winter's cold air sting my nostrils. I looked down and hugged the front of my peacoat, pulling it closer to my body while I carefully tried to avoid stepping into the hard-edged mini-craters of soil made jagged and sharp by the thawing and refreezing cycles that alternate at this time of year.

"This lot must be a muddy mess when it rains," I said.

"Probably. But just breathe in this country air. No bad odors."

And no homeless people hunched against the city parking lot's walls, I thought. No anonymous figures walking silently toward us as we hasten our pace to the bar's entrance. No reason to figure out the best way to escape a pickpocket or someone worse in case one of those anonymous figures turned against us at the last second. No tug of war between the pangs of guilt and the need for self-preservation when we admit to ourselves that we racially profile one of our own.

I turned toward Marie. "So how did you know about this place?"

"A friend of a friend mentioned it to me last summer. I was curious, so I came out here with Karen." Marie paused. "That was before Karen and I stopped seeing each other, of course."

"Of course," I said.

"Anyway, everyone seemed friendly, especially after a couple of beers."

"How's the music?"

"The Country and Western was on heavy rotation the first time I was here. But the second time, there was a black deejay. She mixed a lot of house music and older R and B. I called and found out she's here tonight."

"Good evening, ladies."

Marie and I looked toward the top of the steps and saw a woman standing in front of the closed door.

Both of her hands were jammed in the side pockets of

her unbuttoned woolen jacket.

"Hi." Marie spoke for both of us.

The woman nodded. "It's Oldies Saturday. We have a two-drink minimum, and like always, no drugs and no smoking on the premises."

Short and solid, with a no-nonsense bearing, the woman's physique and brusque way of speaking convinced me she'd been chosen to be the club's bouncer. When she reached past my chest to open the door, I saw a canister of Mace hooked to her belt and that vision convinced me firmly that she was the club's rule enforcer.

We heard the rough, uneven sounds of static buzz through the woman's jacket.

She didn't flinch. Nor did she attempt to respond to the voice at the other end of the walkie-talkie.

I wanted to believe Marie when she said we'd be fine coming to this bar, but I knew if my life depended upon it, I wouldn't be able to look at a map and tell anyone exactly where we were. I didn't know anything about the bar's clientele, and yes, I did care about that. I had to care about that.

"Do you ever need to use that Mace?" I asked the bouncer.

The woman's lips formed a half smile. "Once in a while we get some teenagers doing a drive by. They like to shout things, you know?" She turned toward a stack of cinder blocks at the top of the steps and reached toward a bottle of beer. She took a swig and continued her answer. "They're basically harmless."

"Okay, if you say so," I said.

"If I didn't think they were harmless, I'd have my gun on my hip instead of this can of pepper spray."

I smiled at the woman, even though I found her words as warm and welcoming as the bar's façade. That is, not at all.

Marie nudged me forward, and we walked into the club.

The first thing I noticed was the bar. The wood and leather-sided rectangle was in the center of the large room. Two women stationed at opposite ends of the bar were working quickly to fill drink orders. The deejay's booth was a small plywood platform tucked into a corner. Mirrors of all shapes and sizes covered most of the walls and bounced the bass lines of an ancient Marvin Gaye tune.

I spied an empty table with two chairs and signaled Marie that I'd claim them.

"Good," Marie said. "I'll get us drinks. What would you like?"

"I'll start with a Coke."

Marvin Gaye morphed into Diana Ross as I headed toward the vacant table.

I walked past several small groups of women. Some were young, most were older, and all of the same ethnicity, neither mine nor Marie's. I sat down and tried my best to make eye contact with the women seated closest to me.

One woman answered my attempts with a smile, so I nodded and smiled back at her.

"Here you are, my dear." Marie handed me a glass of soda as she pulled out her chair and sat down. She held up her hand and gestured toward the room. "What do you think so far?"

"It's not Señora's."

"Yeah. The lighting's completely different. And the women aren't glammed up."

"And there's only three of us women of color here. You, me, and the deejay." I turned to get a better look at the music player.

She was young. Too young for it to ever cross her mind that all the plaid flannel shirts and the two posters advertising the upcoming gun show at the Grange might be clues for her to be careful out here. She wore her hair in long dreads gathered together with ribbon at her neckline and descending like narrow ropes down her back. She was a study in constant motion, dividing her attention between a knot of women waiting to talk with her and the twin turntables all set for her to transition from one song to another. She seemed to know the women who awaited her attention, and she acknowledged their music requests with a nod and a self-confident smile.

Marie watched me watching the deejay. "What do you think of the music?"

"So far, so good."

"Wanna dance?" she asked.

I touched my chest and feigned surprise.

"Me? No thanks. I dance better in my head than I do with my feet."

Marie laughed.

A woman sitting at an adjoining table must have read our lips, because she came right over and extended her hand to Marie, who jumped up and glided her way to the dance floor.

I watched my friend move fluidly with her dance partner, and I began to relax. Although we were in a place that was new to me and semi-new to Marie, it was familiar territory, a place that offered us the freedom to drink, dance, laugh, fall in or out of love or lust with a woman, and not be judged for any of it. It offered us space to simply be who we were.

The deejay gave David Bowie, Janet Jackson, and Drake their turns to coax dancers onto the floor, and Marie kept up with each song.

Seconds after the transition to Sylvester's "Mighty Real," Marie gestured her exhaustion and returned to our table. She put her beer bottle to her lips and took a long drink. "I'm getting too old for this."

"Nonsense. It looked like you were keeping up with your dance partner."

"That's because the deejay plays a lot of old stuff that I used to dance to."

The lights dimmed slightly, and Bonnie Raitt's voice drew a contingent of dancers to the floor.

Marie looked at me. "So, tell me, Jaie, do you miss Terez?"

I focused on a pair of dancers who held each other tightly. "I'm really not in the mood to talk about her."

Marie nodded. "I'm getting another beer. Are you ready for something stronger than Coke?"

The intimate dancers reminded me of the evening so long ago when I first saw Terez standing in the rear room of the women's bar in Allerton. That first glance suggested the profound intimacy we'd come to know and experience.

"Yes, please." I reached in my pocket for my wallet and

withdrew some money. "Could you get me a scotch, neat?"

"You got it."

Rick James's reedy voice covered Bonnie Raitt's final notes as Marie walked toward the bar.

Just then, an angry, high-pitched voice split the air.

"Stop playing all that nigger music!"

Marie must have heard the ear-piercing command as clearly as I had. She stood stock still for a second, turned around, and walked toward me.

The deejay stared at the space above the heads of the women who stood closest to her platform. I saw her expressionless eyes as mine tried to telegraph, are you okay?

Rick James's lyrics grew louder as they filled the room, suddenly depleted of human voices.

I stood and put on my jacket. I gathered Marie's from the back of her chair and handed it to her as soon as she was close enough to reach for it. Without saying a word to each other, we walked toward the door.

Outside the temperature felt twice as cold as when we arrived an hour earlier.

"Ladies, leaving so soon?" the bouncer asked.

Before we could answer, we heard tires squealing and saw an old truck speed by the parking area.

A young man's sneer played substitute for the truck's passenger side window.

"Faggots! Fucking faggots!" he yelled.

"See what I mean?" the bouncer said. "They don't even know this is a women's bar. They're stupid but harmless."

"Yup," I said, as Marie and I began our walk to her car.

I turned back to speak to the bouncer.

"Why bother with those teenagers' hateful insults when the more dangerous hatred is inside the club?"

"What? What do you mean?" the bouncer asked.

I didn't stop to explain my comment. I just kept walking with total disregard for the parking lot's ruts and uneven rocks that tried to disrupt my progress.

In the days and months that followed, I did talk to Marie about that night and about that bar.

We mentioned the young dreadlocked deejay, and we

asked each other if we should have invited her to leave the bar with us. Marie called to find out if she'd returned to her platform and its turntables after that night's incident. She hadn't.

I still go to Señora's once in a while, because from time to time I need to hear loud throbbing music, drink overpriced scotch, and feel that particular kind of energy that only exists where we lesbians gather to enjoy ourselves. I have to admit though, whenever a deejay is in the middle of an extended R and B set, I always hear that bigoted woman's hard-edged voice spitting out her poisonous command, and I feel a little less safe in a space that used to offer me shelter.

WHEELS TO THE POLLS

Despite the bad weather, I have something I must do today. It's a good thing I just bought this waterproof, hooded jacket. I don't know how far I'll have to go from the bus to the community college's gym, and I don't intend to get wet, especially since I've finally landed a beautician who knows how to fix my hair. After months of just making do, I look like myself again, waves, curls, and all.

My daughter offered to drive me to the college, but my new, motorized chair won't fit in her small car. She reminded me half-a-dozen times that there were easier ways for me to do this task, but I haven't reached that stage where I'm ready to do what's easy. My pride is intertwined with my independence.

Besides, I'm eager to use my new set of wheels. I expect I can go just about anywhere now, and faster than before. Look how quickly my new chair got me from my apartment to the building's front door, and beyond it to the community's bus.

"Good morning, Ms. Sims."

"Good morning to you, Mr. Mack."

I like this new driver. He's polite, respectful, and he doesn't assume he can call all his passengers by their first names.

"Let me secure these anchors and operate the lift for you, Ms. Sims. Then we'll be ready to take off."

"Take your time, Mr. Mack. The college gym isn't far and the polls will be open for eight more hours."

"You're right." Mr. Mack chuckled. "Too bad it's raining. I ordered good weather for Election Day, but nobody listened to me."

"Oh, a little rain won't stop me," I said.

As the bus turned from the long driveway and edged its way to the main thoroughfare, I thought about my parents and their parents before them.

The weather conditions never prevented them from voting even though they always had to wait until the end of their workdays before they walked miles and miles to get to the polls. My grandfather Alfred lived in West Virginia. He always arrived at the polls covered from head to foot in that day's coal dust.

My other grandfather, Dugger, lived, worked, and voted in Accomack County, Virginia. He'd arrive at the polls with his clothes still damp and reeking of ocean brine and the oysters he'd shucked that day before sending them to the processing line in Virginia's largest oyster canning company.

My grandmother Birdie taught children in the local normal school, and my other grandma, Rose, worked as a housekeeper in other peoples' homes. After women were granted the right to vote, they always went to the polls dressed as neatly as pins and prepared to answer questions. Back then, most of the clerks were determined to thin the ranks of "the coloreds" before they stepped front and forward to cast their votes in the open, all-too-visible excuses for booths.

Once when I was very young, I overheard my grandmother Birdie talking about privacy and the secret ballot.

"That was a myth," she told my mother. "They knew who we voted for because they stood by and watched us closer than a fly on a piece of honey cake."

Secret ballot or not, tired and work-worn, they always voted. So did my mother and so do I.

The other bus passengers and I exchanged greetings and then fell silent.

The quiet didn't bother me because I didn't want to talk to anyone about our mission. I simply wanted to accomplish it, not discuss it. I'd noticed several of the residents who lived on my floor had affixed the American flag to their apartment doors. I suspected I knew what that suggested, but I was never one hundred percent sure. I always waited to see how my neighbors related to me before I decided if their patriotism was inclusive of folks who didn't look like them.

I talked about politics with my family, though. My

grandparents always voted for the party of Lincoln. My parents were registered Democrats. I'd always cast my votes for the party of Kennedy, Clinton, Barack Obama, and once again for Clinton. My daughter and her spouse have voted for whichever progressive candidates promised to push for their rights.

The rain slicked streets didn't slow our journey, and we were parked at the college before we knew it.

The second Mr. Mack lowered the lift and assured me I was all set to go, I put my chair in gear and the two of us, my chair and I, made short work of the distance to the gym.

A group of people wearing campaign buttons and perfunctory smiles stood near the gym's entrance. One of the button wearers bent down to speak to me.

"Hello. May I give you a pamphlet?" she asked.

"No thanks." If I didn't know by now for whom to cast my vote, I shouldn't be here.

"Good morning." A second person practically curtsied in front of me. "You know, you could have filled out an absentee ballot instead of coming out here in the rain."

I looked up and stared straight into her eyes.

"I know you mean well, dear, but why on earth would I do that?" I asked. "I couldn't have known it was going to rain today, and I'm not absent. You can see I'm capable of being here."

Before the young woman could react, I rolled my way to the sign-in table and pointed to my name in the registered voters' directory. The line leading to the voters' booths moved quickly, and before I knew it, I'd done my civic duty.

As I motored away from the gym, I saw the absentee-ballot-suggestion woman wave good-bye to me and my chair.

"Thanks for coming out," she yelled to my back.

I couldn't suppress a grin when I heard her say that, because it reminded me of my daughter's tale about the poll workers who'd said that very thing to her a few elections ago. She told me she'd answered, "No problem. Coming out to my family was much more challenging than coming out to vote."

Mr. Mack watched as I returned to the bus.

"Well it didn't take you long to vote, Ms. Sims." He maneuvered my chair and me onto the lift.

"Sometimes it just goes that way," I said. "And this particular 'sometimes' is unlike any other I've ever experienced."

Three of my fellow passengers were already seated.

"It's like the rise of Hitler all over again," one of them said.

"And it's up to people like us to do something about it," a second person said.

I looked in the direction of that person's voice and saw a gentleman whose thick, white hair was partially obscured by one of those Irish woolen tweed caps I'd always loved.

The man looked at me, his eyes filled with an expression of understanding bolstered by the wisdom of experience.

I nodded his way.

"Thank you for voting."

I studied the faces of the other bus riders. To a person, they all smiled at me. I realized I probably wasn't the only one on that bus who had pressed the button above the list of all the Democrat candidates. Of course, I couldn't be completely sure about that. Even so, I thanked them with my eyes and my smile. And I gave thanks to all the other "thems" who'd gone before me and died or spilled blood or walked miles in work-stained clothes and thin-soled shoes, all to advance our rights and procure equal treatment for their children and mine.

The ride back to our retirement community wasn't as quiet as the ride to the polls had been. We talked to each other and agreed to meet for lunch or dinner at least once a month. Going forward we'd call ourselves the SCAD GROUP, Seniors Care About Democracy. And we resolved we'd summon all our energies and go to the polls each Election Day for as long as we could get there, and after that for as long as we could fill out one of those new Vote-By-Mail ballots.

I'd do it to memorialize my parents and their parents and to remind my daughter that she comes from a line of people who struggled to go the polls, who cherished a right for which so many who went before them perished.

POEMS

POETRY...

Is the sound my pen makes

when my heart explodes onto paper,

or,

mends and beats rhythmically

once again.

WORDS WITHOUT END, AMEN

Words never end.
One poem calls for another.
A short story begs to be longer
Songs cry out for more lyrics.
A novel demands a sequel,
Its characters plead for more time.
Love letters, resumes, thank-you notes, shopping lists
spin out of control,
Serial emails and text messages
Unravel like balls of yarn.
We tap "Reply" so often
we lose the beginning.

Words never end.
They spill from my eyes
And trickle down my cheek.
They leave a trail of letters
just like that last instant message,
The one I won't answer
For fear you won't either.

CAN I SIMPLY BE?

For all the women whose ethnicity,
age, size, and lesbian identity
are questioned by their so-called lovers.
Can I be me?
Simply me,
without a swagger or an attitude at half-mast?
Can I speak with
clipped syllables, words spelled correctly, pre-edited
before they come tumbling out?
May I appear,
with wiry white curls entwined with darker ones,
in disdain of the dye bowl?

Can I be me?

Simply me,
one size larger than my photo,
the one taken during a year of grief
and remain qualified for your attention?
Can I be neither club butch nor high-heeled femme?

Please understand,
if I cannot be me,
simply me,
then you and I cannot be
we.

LONG STORY SHORT

Back in the days

of fiancés

I sat astride my first barstool

in a North Philly corner spot.

Me, him, and the future mom-in-law

eager to see if I could hold my own.

A scotch for him,

A beer for her.

"And what about you, baby?"

asked the barmaid,

winking and wise beyond her paygrade.

"Bourbon and ginger, please."

"You got it, baby."

And I did.

"Baby" said twice, confirmed what I'd felt and run from

at the most awkward times.

"Baby" heard twice, was all it took

to make me wonder

how many women would call me

other than my name

before I'd own who I am

and feel perfectly

okay about it.

NO LOVE SONG

This is not a love song.

It's not a necklace of words strung together sweetly

for our benefit.

This is not a romance poem,

Not a tale following a formula

that must end happily.

This is not a guitar pulsing

and racing across the strings of our needy hearts.

It is not a moody saxophone

vibrating inside our disaffected souls.

It is a balm, a distraction from the lonely moments,

a response to all the smug ones who dismiss our pleas

and dispense their ineffective prescriptions.

"Write yourself a few poems,
then call me in the morning," they say.

This is not a love song,

Not a love song.

But I'll sing the lyrics just the same.

BETWEEN A ROCK AND A SOFT PLACE

Most days
I face the wind
and challenge its gusts to reshape me.
I refuse to bend with its currents.

Most days
I confront the rain
and dare the pebble-sharp drops
to send me in search of shelter.
I don't rust when I'm wet.

Most days
I stare defiantly at the sun
and forbid it to sear my skin.
I don't burn and blister under its white, hot heat.

But,
once in a while,
when I lower my gaze and turn my back,
I feel a breeze caress my throat.
I taste the raindrops that quench my thirst.
I feel my soul ignite, courtesy of the golden rays,
and I believe I am beautiful,

if only for that moment.

THE WEATHER

Freezing rain

is simply

water falling from the sky,

naively enrobing

the ground, streets, tree limbs, cars

and hearts

already numb,

frozen by winter's early arrival.

I have heard that

everything thaws, given enough time and hope.

NOTE FOUND ON THE FLOOR

Memo to those who have inquired:

She has stopped writing poems,

because words are simply organized letters

that neither slow nor speed the voyage to anger's end.

They fail to cushion the crash.

To all who keep asking:

She's not planning to dream any more poetry.

She's abandoned pen and paper

in favor of living gracefully

and chasing sleep bereft of dreams.

In case you still have questions:

All the poetry is mowed down.

The path to her heart is now dense with weeds
whose tangled growth chokes all breath.

And her gardener

has taken on a different job.

ELLE M'ATTEND (SHE WAITS FOR ME)

She waits for me at the top of the stairs,

Her smile now a flat line of non-acceptance,

Her glance the model of disapproval.

My bloodied knees, twin symbols of scarlet shame

as embarrassment closes my face

like slats of room-darkening blinds.

"You were rough-housing again," she says.

"You need to act like a young lady."

Cowboys and cops and space travelers are who I am,
I want to say…but don't.

She waits for me in the living room,

Eyes trained on the pages of a book whose characters
do not disappoint her.

I enter, arms cold beneath
the sleeves of a summer blouse
testing October's chill.

"William would have offered you his jacket," she says.

William, heir to light skin, good hair,
and the pint of scotch
tucked in the back seat
of his father's car.

"I was out with George who lent me his sweater."

Donna or Marie might lend me their hearts if I'd ask,
I want to say…but don't.

She waits for me in the kitchen,

A post-work cigarette poised between two fingers,

as smoke curls beyond nails reddened with polish.

I toss off my fear, stand tall, and state who I love,

She invites me to leave, then adds,

"Phone me once in a while…

so I know you're still alive."

I'll call in time,

alive and whole,

truthful and no longer hidden.

CLOSER THAN SKIN AND TEETH, HER STORY AND MINE

Your face glazed in grief

as you look beyond the outline of mine

and speak of being alone.

You bow your head in deference to

the goddess of regret with whom you spent time

in the small house that grew larger

each day you were alone.

I listen quietly.

My unspoken memories sentenced to an indeterminate

term of silence.

I do not mention the days my sense of self

turned inside out

and I no longer recognized who I was.

Now, as you describe the coat of agony you wore,

I listen, nod, and pay my respects.

Later, I'll ask the air to whom I can confess my struggle

to live alongside shame and

overcome hurt that was closer

than skin and teeth.

That pain is now dull.

It fades away,

unspoken, but visible

if you were to look for it

after reminiscing about yours.

THE FLIPSIDE

I acknowledge my lack of formal training in writing poetry. I
thank Gwendolyn Brooks, Langston Hughes, Robert Frost, Nikki
Giovanni, Sonia Sanchez, W.H. Auden, Carolyn Rodgers, June
Jordan, and Cheryl Clarke who showed me a poem can do
whatever it pleases.

There's always a flipside.

Part B, the back side of Part A.

A tune we barely recognize

confuses feet used to dancing up-tempo,

and mouths all set to lip-synch lyrics we know.

Have we flipped for the sake of symmetry,

or simply for humanity's

refusal to hold close that which is right and just?

And yes, this is personal,

because poems often are.

And yes, this is political,

because poems can be activists

marching through the streets,

chanting syllables against those who flip

the Lilly Leadbetters, prison reform,

marriage equality, tolerance for the newcomers,

the little boy who touched Obama's hair,

and all who wanted to do the same.

The hopes that once lifted us

now lay dispersed,

withered among the hatred and cowardice.

Flip the flipside

and restore the music that brings us joy!

* Written with Toni Morrison resting somberly in my mind.

PROSE POEM: IT ISN'T...AND THEN, IT IS

My April 2020 blog included a few ironic/amusing moments that arrived with Covid-19.

Now we're near the end of May and the gloves are off, metaphorically speaking. Humor is taking a nap while lost jobs, daily death statistics, incompetence, a dearth of empathy, the inevitable result of stupidity, refusals to stave off disease by staying at home, selfish neediness of l-want-it-now, and the failure to understand how mask-less close-ups lead to more illness and dying have taken the place of humor and inspired this prose poem.

It's *not* my grandfather's lot of unloading food and bullets headed to the muddy mustard-gas-filled trenches,

while images of *his* grandfather's back, bent under the weight of tobacco he never owned,

flashed before his eyes, reminding him to leave the oyster cannery if given a second chance.

It's *not* my grandmother's frustration, etched in chalk dust that settled

upon children's shoulders as they learned in their under-supplied, unheated Virginia classroom,

and then followed her to Pennsylvania,

where her color nullified her credentials

and obliged her to wait tables in a tearoom.

It's *not* the yoke my father bore as he
earned bed and board while studying
trigonometry and German,

before wearing the uniform and intercepting
enemy messages from Japanese planes

destined to collide with American fire over
the red-stained Pacific.

It's *not* the self-righteous anger boiling
from the anti-war/poverty/racism placards

hoisted above the heads of my generation

to protest the napalm and knife-sharp bamboo

that sliced through bloody feet in jungles
thousands of miles away.

It is *none* of those things.

It *is* the slow torching of our sanity when
we hear the senseless ramblings and the
truths that disappear like wisps of smoke
floating from visibility.

It *is* the nonstop pain of absence when a
loved one most needs our presence.

It *is* the fear that keeps us company every
time we leave our front door and tentatively
breathe in the unknown.

It *is* the silence in our workplace, our

school, our site of worship, our familiar streets.

It *is* the contemptible weakness of those we counted on to be strong, to resist the commands to return the innocent to school, to attend to the droplets of illness that bring us to our knees.

It *is* our head-spinning free fall into sacrificing those who are poor, old, or infirm.

It is *us*.

And we know better.

We know how to *be* better.

Will we?

Now?

THEY'RE BACK AGAIN

They're back again.

The young ones who march, then leave their words

strewn at our feet,

hoping we'll read them

since we refused to listen.

They're back again.

The disaffected older ones who watch the marchers,

then saunter to Facebook and write,

"I've seen all this before. Where did it get us?"

They're back again.

The oldest ones who've seen quite enough,

but still inhale equality and exhale their hopes
entwined in poetic syllables.

They're back again.

All the ones who believed a poem could make us dance

and turn the world toward kindness,

if only for one generation.

They're back again, back again,

Spending their poems like there's no tomorrow.

Charging their efforts to a credit card of words

stacked against the costs of moral poverty.

They're back again.

They're back again.

Welcome them back.

ALL THE DIFFERENT PEOPLE I'VE BEEN (IN POLITE TERMS, OF COURSE)

Female infant, colored.

Female student, negro.

Female college undergrad, black.

Female grad student, Afro-American.

Female teacher, African American.

Retired educator, person of color.

Writer, BIPOC.

The mind fractures

in response to which box to check.

Other minds become spinning wheels

set to stop at Spanish-speaking, Hispanic,

Mestizo, Chicano, Dominican,

'Rican, Boricua, Latino, Latina, Latinx,

'Cajun, Creole, Gechee,

Why is it

that all of this time,

those who label *us*

have remained simply

white?

OPINIONS AND ASSORTED

THOUGHTS

WEAVING MY HERSTORY INTO MY FICTION

While I'm not a new *writer* per se, I am new to writing fiction for publication. I'm not formally taught in the ways of writers, but I've found there's a beauty and grace attached to that. While I don't want to be an editor's worst nightmare, I do enjoy the license to tweak rules and play with all kinds of devices, like narrative style, point of view, and character development.

Dare I alternate my chapters between first- and third-person narrative? Why not? No one told me I couldn't. Can I spin my stories well enough to convince a publisher to print them, even if they are stories about black lesbian relationships? I have nothing to lose but time, and I won't lose that if I'm enjoying my work.

I'd like to jump feet first into a plot about two black women from totally different socioeconomic worlds who spot each other during the festival that is their lives and decide to try life's dance together. I don't see why I can't do that. I'm willing to bet there's a readership of black, same-sex-loving women who are hungry to see their stories between a book's covers. For that reason alone, I'm more than willing to leap without a safety net into uncharted waters.

But have I really done that? Have I taken that risk and written about the unknown, or have I created plots and characters borrowed from familiar territory? I need to be honest with my readers and with myself and confess that I've used bits and pieces of my personal history in writing three novels thus far. In committing my characters to the computer screen, I couldn't escape my past and present realities any more than I could walk on my hands for a mile while singing my favorite Gladys Knight and the Pips song.

For me, what's inescapable are the settings of my stories. My familiar Philadelphia and its suburbs, an urban public high school, a large university, sections of Cape Cod, a home construction company's office.

What flows most naturally from my imagination are African American female characters of all colors and backgrounds. What intrigues me the most are storylines involving women whose needs attract them to one another despite their differences. The frequently difficult "fit" between two people of color who were raised to believe they should oppose each other instead of mesh is a theme that easily bubbles its way to the surface.

It surfaced quickly when I started writing *Breaking Jaie*.

My history includes Mary Franklin, my best friend and third-grade classmate when we attended Samuel K. Faust Elementary School. Mary and I were two little "colored" girls enrolled in a school district that was predominantly white. Day after day, we shared insider jokes and Graham crackers, and we made sure we always sat next to each other during our morning and afternoon rides aboard the yellow bus. I remember wanting our laughter to continue during after-school homework sessions or Saturday visits to Mary's house or to mine. And I recall not understanding why Mary could never accept my invitations to visit.

Mary understood, though. She fully grasped the implications of our school bus stopping so I could get off at Garfield Lane along with the other kids who lived in Concord Park, a purposefully planned interracial neighborhood, while she exited the bus a few blocks later, with the kids who lived in Linconia, the predominantly black neighborhood on the "other side of Concord Drive."

No doubt Mary's parents were up front with their daughter and explained their version of why she and I couldn't be more than school and bus mates.

I didn't understand the barriers of caste and class until the passage of time delivered more incidents and awakened me to their existence. There were times when I felt myself suspended like a drop of oil in a vat of water, caught between the ever-present distrust I saw in the eyes of a few other Mary Franklins I tried to befriend and the charitable disdain I noticed leaching from the pores of the light-bright Jack and Jill members whose friendships and social events eluded my comfort zone. I lacked that group's mandatory membership qualifications: correct complexion, appropriate hair texture, parents who were doctors, lawyers, judges, or wealthy funeral directors.

My personal history is alive in my fiction. My memories breathe within the bodies and spirits of Jaie Baxter and Terez Overton in *Breaking Jaie,* along with Corey Lomax and Kinshasa Jordan in *Leave of Absence.*

During my teaching career, I met a few Jaie Baxters, girls whose academic potential was feared, trashed, and discarded by insecure and desperately unhappy mothers. I've lived in Terez's and Kinshasa's skin all my life, unabashedly comfortable, but aware of my need to expand my points of view.

I hope bookstores, brick and mortar as well as virtual businesses, will make room for my books and for those of other lesbian writers of color. And I hope that readers will find our books and enjoy reading them, even if the fiction contains bits and pieces of the authors' realities.

THE DOG DAYS OF AUGUST
or
A TALE OF TWO DIVAS

This month's blog was supposed to be about our annual yard sale: the good, the bad, and the amusing. But Aretha Franklin's death leaves me sitting here at my desk, grappling with all manner of thoughts and reminiscences.

Paramount are my memories of singing along and dancing as Aretha's voice wound itself around me. I can still see the tiny patch of checkerboard-pattern linoleum floor at Babe and Frank's, an eatery across the street from my K-8 elementary school. That's where my more extroverted classmates demonstrated the latest dance steps, while those of us who ate lunch there only on "orchestra day" would blend the aromas of cheeseburgers and fried onions with the sounds cooking in the jukebox.

There were countless basement parties where we danced to 45 rpm records orbiting the stem of the turntable. Aretha made her presence known during my junior and senior proms, as well as during the parties held at Curtis Hall. DJs spun her records along with the best of Motown while the bands took their break.

Four days ago (mid-August, 2018), trump used the word "dog" to describe Omarosa Manigault, the president's aide he had fired. Today he lauded Aretha Franklin's talent.

It's uncanny how I can remember the lyrics of many of Aretha's songs, but I have to think long and hard to recall what I ate for breakfast a day ago. I know long-term and short-term memories reside in different areas of our brains, but maybe Aretha's music lingers because of the emotions it stirred. If "touch memory" exists, how about "feeling memory" as well?

The recollections of Aretha singing during presidential inaugurations, performances at the White House, in Paris's

Olympia Theater, at the Uptown Theater in Philly, in my parents' living room, in my own family room, and through the headphones encasing my ears are as much a part of my life now as they've always been.

If you feel the power of music but don't play an instrument nor possess the talent necessary to give voice to your emotions, you're joyful there are others who can play the music and sing the songs for you.

What songs would Aretha choose to sing today? It seems her demands for RESPECT have fallen on deaf ears. AIN'T NO WAY you can convince me that, collectively, we Arethas who live in the United States right now are respected because of our humanity as well as our citizenship. Not now, when we're facing concerted efforts to push us back into the ugliest era in our nation's history. We women of color would be links in a long CHAIN OF FOOLS if we ignored that which confronts us today, the ignorance and fear of those who are different, the unhealthy desire to accumulate and hold on to power and money, and the hate-fueled determination to continue debasing us.

Despite their many differences, Omarosa Manigault and Aretha Franklin have their racial and gender identities in common. They are/were black women. Labeling one the Queen of Soul cannot erase the anger I feel when he labels the other person a dog.

We are all Omarosa! We are all Aretha!

WILL THE REAL DR. DONALD SHIRLEY PLEASE STAND UP?

The announcement of this year's Oscar for Best Motion Picture left some filmgoers stunned and others happy.

The Green Book tells the story of Dr. Donald Shirley, a professional pianist of color, and his white driver/bodyguard, Tony Lip, as they motor through America's southern states during Dr. Shirley's performance tour.

Contrary to one's expectation that most black filmgoers would laud the movie's Oscar victory, the aftermath of its first-place status elicited unexpected reactions. A number of black film critics joined Dr. Shirley's family members who scorned the "untruths" presented in the movie.

Among the film's inaccuracies are the portrayal of Dr. Shirley's having been raised by a single mother who struggled against poverty, the pianist's issue with alcoholism, his possession of a throne upon which he sat as he interviewed Tony Lip, his distaste for fried chicken, his emotional distance and lack of awareness of popular black musicians, and his estrangement from black culture.

I believe the film's truth-bending scenes serve the filmmaker's purpose of reaching a wide audience, one that would understand Dr. Shirley *only* with the insertion of hyperbole and a few distortions of the facts of his life.

It's possible the movie's producers realized this and tailored the script to fit different viewers.

FOR AUDIENCE MEMBERS WHOSE RELATIONSHIPS WITH PEOPLE OF COLOR HAVE BEEN SUPERFICIAL AND LESS THAN MEANINGFUL...

Although the portrayal of the heretofore racist Tony Lip as Dr. Shirley's "guide to black culture" is patronizing at best, it serves as a gold-leafed invitation to filmgoers who have never established a deep relationship with a person of color. Tony's role provides comfort and sends a message of safety to many   of those ticket buyers. It telegraphs *yes-the-movie-is-about-racism-and-its-inherent-violence-against-black-people, but-it's-safe-for-you-to-see-it-because-Dr.-Shirley-isn't-killed-and-the-movie's-real-hero-is-Tony-Lip, a white man.* Perhaps the success of this messaging effort explains Viggo Mortenson's Best Actor nomination alongside Mahershala Ali's Best Supporting Actor nod. Ali won…the second-place award.

The Green Book is 2018's *Lilies of the Field*. They are both emotionally satisfying films whose endings promise audiences that everything will work out as well as the happiness evidenced by the smiling faces surrounding the Christmas dinner table chez Lip.

FOR AMERICAN PEOPLE OF COLOR WHO HAVE CONSIDERED RAGE WHEN FEAR IS SIMPLY TOO MUCH…

Black filmgoers approached *The Green Book* with a mixture of curiosity and a sort of pre-viewing relief. We read the reviews that mentioned Dr. Shirley survived the most harrowing moments of his tour of the South. We wouldn't have to endure the pain that accompanies our memories of race relations during the 1950s. We wouldn't have to still our hands or quicken our breaths in fearful expectation of having to witness the inevitable, sickening, and oft-repeated fate of those who went before us, headlong, into enemy territory.

We can eat our popcorn and smile at Dr. Shirley's triumphs. We can lose ourselves in imaginary moments when color, gender, or sexuality won't hold us back.

FOR LGBTQIA PEOPLE OF COLOR WHO HAVE CONSIDERED SCREAMING WHEN THE RAINBOW FLAG, PRIDE MONTH, AND OUR ACHIEVEMENTS HAVE NOT BEEN ENOUGH…

This is the group in which I belong. I absorbed every

frame of *The Green Book*, perhaps because I related to Dr.
Shirley's character and to some of his experiences. When I
read about the film's inaccuracies, I felt disappointed. In
retrospect, I welcomed spinning through each distortion or
omission and questioning the filmmaker's motives. Perhaps
the "invented" material existed for the benefit of viewers
who might not have grasped the subtleties of Dr. Shirley's
background and how that background impacted the pianist's
life.

Dr. Shirley's mother was a teacher and his father, an
Episcopal priest. These two facts granted the family upper
middle-class status. The subtlety of class difference
inherent in Episcopal vs. other Protestant sects is not easily
discerned by people who don't realize there IS a black upper
middle-class.

According to his family members, Dr. Shirley was not
addicted to alcohol, nor did he drink Cutty Sark each night
to drown the indignities he experienced. Why did the
filmmaker insert that falsehood? Was it to suggest the
pianist could not have been strong enough—read that man
enough—to endure the indignities foisted upon him because
of his race and sexuality? Was it to state that he could not
have been successful without leaning on a liquid crutch?

Although Dr. Shirley maintained strong friendships
with Duke Ellington, Lionel Hampton, Count Basie,
Leontyne Price, Paul Robeson, and William Warfield, his
black contemporaries in the music world, he experienced an
emotional disconnect from people of color who lived in
extreme poverty.

That's why the film's chord that sounded truest to me
was the silence-filled scene of Shirley emerging from his
rented car, that was stopped by the side of the road, and
looking at the black farm workers standing in the field
across from him. He stared at them and they stared at him.
Each face wore the expression of people who had known
each other once, a long time ago. Shadows of tentative
recognition blended with the impossibility of relationship,
and those shadows met in the middle of the road that
separated them like a gaping chasm carved by the knives of
one person's opportunities and the others' lack of it.

Those of us who belonged to this third audience saw Dr. Shirley's existential plight.

He was a person unable to be whole, unable to merge the different layers of his identity: a black man in America, a black man who communed frequently with white Americans, a black man educated abroad, a black man who performed European classical music with as much skill as he performed popular jazz, a black man whose same-gender attractions left him vulnerable to violence and arrests.

In case anyone missed Dr. Shirley's plight, the screenwriter provided his character a stirring "who am I" soliloquy delivered at the apex of his frustration, in the middle of a rain-drenched road, in the middle of the American South.

The speech was far from subtle. It was the film's exclamation point.

Some of us have been there. Some of us are there. Some of us will find ourselves there.

HIDDEN WORDS

Do you remember having to write book reports? I do.

Every student who attended the Philadelphia High School for Girls was required to write a book report each quarter of the semester. We selected our books from the school's library list, which was organized by grade level and literary genre.

During my sophomore year, the chairman of the English Department, Dr. Jack Edelson, was my teacher. Dr. Edelson, a man whose affect suggested a lack of passion about most issues other than William Shakespeare's plays and Homer's dramatic metaphors, began each semester's quarter by explaining which genre we had to read to fulfill that quarter's book report requirement. With the school's library list propped on our desks, we listened as Dr. Edelson narrated a description of every book included in the quarter's chosen genre. He filled every moment of that day's class describing plots, characters, settings, and themes. And we placed a check mark next to the titles whose details sounded interesting.

Our second quarter's genre was poetry, and Dr. E. shared tidbits of information about each of the poets listed in our library booklet.

With great enthusiasm, I entered the school's library in search of a volume of e.e. cummings's poetry. Failing to find any, I looked for a collection of Robert Frost's poems. Obviously, my classmates had borrowed those books before I got there, because none was left. Somewhat frustrated, I began to pay more attention to the poets' names than to the titles inscribed on the books' spines. Before long, I spotted a name I'd heard my parents mention. Langston Hughes. I read the book's preface and its first poem. I'd struck gold. When I re-examined the tenth-grade poetry list, I didn't find any mention of Hughes. Undaunted and by now smitten with the promise of discovering something akin to magic, I signed out *Montage of a Dream Deferred* and took a chance that Dr. E. would approve of my choice.

From that day on, Langston Hughes was no longer hidden from me. I'd uncovered his words and I'd uncovered his identity...or so I thought.

During the next several decades, as I grew comfortable with the totality of my identity, I became curious about the intersectionality of black and LGBTQ literature. Had both been impacted in the same ways by the shifts in political, economic, and social changes in the U.S.?

Much has been written about the Harlem Renaissance (1918-1935) and its writers, musicians, and artists, some of whom, although married to opposite-gender spouses, were gay, lesbian, or bisexual.

In describing that period, Dr. Henry Louis Gates wrote, "[That period was] ...surely as gay as it was black, not that it was exclusively either of these." {*The Black Man's Burden*, 1993.}

It was the post-WWI era, when Black soldiers returning from the European battlefields hoped to be greeted as heroes, or at least loyal patriots. Instead, they encountered the same state of racism with which they'd lived before enlisting in the armed forces. Because of the closures of the urban war-materials factories, soldiers returned to rising unemployment. Despite these two realities, many Black WWI vets landed service-industry jobs. Employment and access to public education led to the emergence of the black middle class, especially in major cities.

De facto segregation in places like New York City, Detroit, and Philadelphia encouraged the formation of racially isolated communities. Within these communities, writers, musicians, and artists knew and supported each other. There were so many stories to be written, so many poems to nurture, so many canvasses to be filled with color, and so many notes to be strung together harmoniously.

The LGBTQ authors were known to each other but not necessarily to their readers. The dangers of being *out* forced these authors to write deeply coded stories. Nonetheless, Richard Bruce Nugent's "Smoke, Lilies, and Jade," which is considered the first published African American gay short story, was less subtle than most of his peers' work. The prose and poetry written by Nella Larson, Angelina Weld-Grimke, Jessie Fauset (a graduate of Phila. High School for Girls), Wallace Thurman, Langston Hughes, Zora Neale Hurston, Countee Cullen, Claude McKay, Alain Locke, and Alice Dunbar-Nelson gave nary a clue to the authors' sexuality.

Most readers were unaware of the masks these writers wore. It wasn't until Weld-Grimke's biographer discovered a diary and love poems written to/about the author's female lovers that rumors about her lesbianism were confirmed.

The Black Arts Movement (late 1950s to 1975) continued the tradition of concealing writers' sexualities. Similar to the Harlem Renaissance, the B.A.M. occurred during a post-war period. Black and white soldiers who survived the extremely unpopular Vietnam conflict returned to anti-war protests, unemployment, and urban unrest. The Civil Rights movement seemed to amble along too slowly for an impatient generation of young blacks who'd been mired in Asian fire fights against yellow people. Those who dared wore "Free Angela" buttons alongside red, green, and black badges, (symbols of Africa's dwarfing the U.S.). Instead of taking their protests to the streets, writers took their creativity to their typewriters and notebooks. What followed was an explosion of poetry, essays, fiction, and plays, all of it dynamic, much of it angry.

Although the B.A.M. was straight-black-male centric, the strong female voices of playwright Lorraine Hansberry, along with poets Carolyn Rodgers, Gayl Jones, Sonia Sanchez, Mari Evans, Nikki Giovanni, Audre Lorde, Cheryl Clarke, and June Jordan were heard as well. With only two exceptions (Lorde and Clarke), these writers didn't reveal their sexuality. They remained under cover and hidden from a significant segment of their audience: the closeted black lesbian readers who searched in vain between countless book covers for some validation of their own existence.

Thank goodness for the arrival of the post-Stonewall era. Most LGBTQ writers, artists, and musicians shed their masks. The words of Audre Lorde, Cheryl Clarke, June

Jordan, Lorraine Hansberry, Alice Walker, Pat Parker, Barbara Smith, Sapphire, Julie Blackwomon, Becky Birtha, Rosa Guy, Alexis DeVeaux, Jewelle Gomez, Michelle Cliff, Shay Youngblood, Jacqueline Woodson, Fiona Zedde, S. Andrea Allen, Lauren Cherelle, Cheril Clarke, Sheree L. Greer, Cheryl Head, Mercedes Lewis, Penny Mickelbury, JP Howard, and I are no longer hidden from our readers.

It is in appreciation of their bravery that I've called out their names. Those whose words were published before mine chanted the courage I needed to be visible and proud to claim the title, black lesbian writer.

SPRING HAS SPRUNG!
Or,
THE WEDDING GIFT

Ah spring! The grass is wearing its lush, baby-green density, a suggestion that anything is possible. For the third year in a row, a purple finch has made her nest in the columnar juniper to the right of our front door. Five hatchlings, beaks open wider than the length of their tiny bodies, greet our curious glances in expectation of their mom's return. Surely, she'll fly in with a takeout meal gathered from the open-air food pantry.

Spring means one thing to my spouse. It's time to go outside and move around some soil.

Viv has weeded the veggie garden, trimmed most of the shrubs, rebuilt and dressed the scarecrow, pulled up and re-laid the walkway pavers that curve from the driveway to the entrance to our home, and scattered grass seed over the bare spots in the lawn.

I've planted a few herbs, prepped the garden boxes for tomato and green bean plants, and most importantly, done a mental review of the quickest way to go to the Patient First facility. This third chore was mandatory.

Although she's neither careless nor accident-prone, Viv gardens with a zealous intensity that often results in a few "Oh-my-God-you're-hemorrhaging," or "Why-are-you-limping?" injuries each gardening season. She made her 2019 inaugural pilgrimage to Patient First less than a week ago after a bite from a mystery insect resulted in my asking, "Oh-my-God-why-is-your-eyelid-all-red-and-swollen-shut?"

A couple of ice-pack sessions and antihistamine tablets later, she was as good as new. Bless her heart.

In addition to spring's perennial reintroduction to the great outdoors, this season is synonymous with proms, graduations, and weddings. My history with all three events is spotty at best. My eighth-grade graduation ceremony included a musical interlude featuring a classmate singing "Moon River" while I accompanied her at the piano. I stumbled only once. Fortunately, the hiccup occurred at the end of the piece, and I attributed the audience's loud applause as their expression of gratitude, as my fingers were able to locate the keys of that last chord.

As for proms, to this day I don't understand how I managed to survive two of them, junior and senior. Trying on gowns, shopping for matching shoes, worrying about the weather and its probable effect on my heat-straightened hair (back in the days of hot combs and curling irons) stressed me the heck out. I went to an all-girls high school, so I didn't have to worry about being invited to the proms. My classmates and I did the choosing and asking. Asking a girl to the prom would have been revolutionary. But in those days, doing so would have bought me an express ticket to a seventy-two-hour hold in a mental health facility.

Weddings are another kettle of fish, aren't they? Unlike proms, weddings continue to occur during the entirety of one's life. For so many years, attending weddings caused me to channel Rupert Everett at his snarkiest. Think *My Best Friend's Wedding.* They also meant I had to wear two costumes. The first was an event-appropriate outfit that invariably involved high heels and makeup, and the second was the mask I wore to conceal who I truly was, along with the anger and despair I felt about being shut out from the institution of marriage. I likened my attending weddings to being a slave forced to celebrate the freedom of others, a freedom I'd never be allowed to enjoy no matter how long my partner and I had been in a loving relationship.

Thank goodness our laws have changed!

In 2013, following the lead of two younger friends, Viv and I got married in Maryland, the closest state to us that had legalized marriage equality. We married two years before the Supreme Court's ruling legalized our unions throughout the nation. Our wedding day and that judicial decision were truly hallelujah moments.

I no longer eschew going to weddings. I've traded my two costumes for whatever feels seasonably comfortable along with the truth about who I am. I hold Viv's hand and we stand proudly close to one another while the couple being joined in marriage exchange their rings and vows. Each same-gender ceremony we attend reinforces the feelings we experienced moments after our ceremony, when we rejoiced in knowing we were equal to every other married couple, straight or gay.

This past May, we were honored to witness the rites of marriage accorded to our neighbor's son, Samuel, and his groom, Gregory. We've known Samuel since they were a child. After the ceremony, we hugged them and handed them their wedding gift.

"It means so much to me that you're here," Samuel said, "because you two were my first queer role models."

Samuel's heartfelt comment was *their* wedding gift to us. Our hearts are full as we celebrate everything that spring offers.

THE LUCKY THIRTEENTH

I've just returned home after attending the thirteenth Golden Crown Literary Society's annual conference. As usual, I've come back filled with many thoughts about writing.

Each GCLS conference has surpassed the one before it, and this particular event was outstanding.

I've always attended the workshops and presentations with notebook and pen in hand, prepared to jot down any workshop presenter's utterance that caught my fancy. At times, making sense of my notes has been a challenge. What I find even more challenging is meeting new people and trying to make chit-chat. I'm a dyed-in-the-wool introvert, shy with a capital "S," and from time to time I'm struck mute in the presence of literary luminaries whose work sits on the shelves of my bookcases. My lower jaw becomes fused to my upper jaw whenever I try to engage these well-known writers in conversation. Thank goodness I seem to write more fluently than I speak.

Imagine how I felt the first time I found myself in the same room (albeit a very large room) with Karin Kallmaker. Try to intuit the paralysis that gripped my entire body the first time I shook Lee Lynch's hand and spoke to Ann Bannon.

As thoroughly as I've enjoyed each GCLS conference I've attended, I've always returned home feeling a bit unsated, still hungry for a more-complete meal. Why? Because the other shelves on my bookcases bear the names of other authors, some of whom I've never met anywhere, not to mention at GCLS conferences. I've devoured the work of Sharon Bridgforth, Fiona Zedde, Nik Nicholson, Becky Birtha, Achy Obejas, Ann Allen Shockley, Cheryl Clarke, Saffire, Nikki Baker, Audre Lorde, Lisa C. Moore, Sheree L. Greer, June Jordan, Dionne Brand, Jacqueline Woodson, and Pat Parker. (Disclosure: I have met Fiona Zedde, and Becky Birtha lived a few streets away from my childhood home. We went to the same high school, and I attended one of her book readings at our neighborhood library.)

Until this thirteenth conference, I never heard anyone mention those names. Although I found some satisfaction in knowing I'd been able to find the work of those writers, I questioned why their names seemed to be nonexistent to most of the conference-goers.

Twice during my two-year tenure as a member of the GCLS's Board of Directors, I suggested that we invite Jewelle Gomez to present the conference's keynote address. It wasn't until after I'd ended my service to the Board that the GCLS presented its Trailblazer Award to Ms. Gomez.

So, this thirteenth annual conference was very meaningful. For the first time, I had the opportunity to listen and speak to a writer of note to whom I could relate on several levels.

When Jewelle spoke the names of writers whose work I'd enjoyed reading and admiring, almost spiritually, I beamed with pride. Had I been connected to EKG wires, the leads would have popped off my skin. When she mentioned the "Black Arts Movement," I nodded in accordance with our shared knowledge, and whispered "Yes!" to the air.

Hadn't I bought every single poetry chapbook the minute it was published by Detroit's Broadside Press and delivered to the Uhuru Kitabu bookstore on Germantown Avenue? Hadn't I read Nikki Giovanni's poem about homosexuality and felt better about myself? Hadn't I grinned upon seeing the title of Carolyn Rodgers's collection, *how I got ovah*?

This conference offered me the gift of my familiar. It validated and restored my connections to literary voices I once knew.

Liz Gibson and her board of directors (including Mary Phillips, the new director) have jumpstarted the effort to make the GCLS a more-inclusive organization. They acted with purpose, intention, and consistency to recognize the ongoing contributions of lesbian writers of color.

The next time I experience a creative spark and some

new inspiration compels me to write, I'll think about the Golden Crown Literary Society's conference, and I'll blame Jewelle Gomez in particular.

THE PERSISTENCE OF HAPPY ENDINGS

There's a rule all writers of romance fiction follow. The story MUST have a happy ending. No matter how many twists and turns roil through the plot, the main characters must celebrate their shared happiness by the time the story concludes.

"But life isn't like that," you say. "Either the protagonist or her new love interest sabotages the relationship. Some issue in their backstory, or some complication preys upon their ability to form a strong union. Sometimes the character suffers an illness and (gasp) dies!"

"Realistic or not," says your editor and/or publisher, "if you're writing a romance novel, it's got to have a happily-ever-after ending. While some rules are made to be broken, this isn't one of them."

You'd think those of us baby boomers would feel reassured by happy endings. After all, every fairy tale our parents read to us and every Nancy Drew/Hardy Boys/ Cherry Ames book we opened had a happy ending. All the Saturday afternoon movies we watched ended with happy resolutions and left us worry free for the rest of the weekend. Each episode's conclusion of *Father Knows Best, My Friend Flicka, The Cisco Kid, Wagon Train, Gunsmoke,* and *Perry Mason* reassured us that right always triumphed over wrong. Even those of us who worried when we watched *Lassie,* the world's most intrepid and intelligent collie, rescue little Timmy from the bottom of the well felt calm and content by the time the show's credits rolled past our eyes.

Of course, the skepticism of adolescence eventually lowered the shade over our eyes, like Venetian blinds at half-mast. We questioned why Ward Bond's aging character never tired of sleeping in a covered wagon. And the evenings when Jim Anderson *(Father Knows Best)* arrived home late, a tad disheveled, had he been playing fast and loose with his secretary? What was the *true* nature of Chester's relationship with Marshall Jim Dillon? Was Miss Kitty in on it? Why didn't anyone ever tell us that Raymond Burr *(Perry Mason)* was a gay man? Knowing his real identity and holding it in front of us like a role model might have persuaded more of us to become criminal lawyers. Or not.

Of course, the question that always lingered in my mind concerned the absence of people who looked like me. Why were people of color missing from the TV screen? *Amos and Andy* and *The Nat King Cole Show* didn't count. We weren't amused by the former, because even then we knew those characters didn't portray any people we knew in real life. And Nat King Cole never sang the songs we liked. Perhaps our parents enjoyed his singing. They used to say his voice was "unique."

My generation was conditioned to expect happy endings. We were sure basic goodness always won, that right prevailed over wrong, the bad guys/gals were always vanquished by the law or by those who wielded the power of law. Even upon learning about the cruelties of slavery, the evils done to America's First Nation peoples, the ugliness inflicted upon Japanese Americans who were interned during World War II, and our government's refusal to allow a ship filled with Jewish passengers fleeing Hitler's death camps to drop anchor in a U.S. port, we continued to cling to the mythology we'd absorbed about our country's penchant for rewarding the efforts of good folks and punishing the evil deeds perpetrated by the bad.

Perhaps it is our persistent habit of creating happy endings that leaves us flummoxed and shaking our heads in disbelief when we hear, see, and read about the chaotic destruction of moral and legal norms raining/reigning down on our country on a daily basis. How can this happen? Where is our happy ending? *Where is our happy ending?*

The 2018 midterm elections showed us a faint glimmer of normalcy. Rebalancing congressional power was a positive beginning. Then we pinned our hopes on the Mueller Report, a document riddled with more redactions than there are holes in a slice of Baby Swiss cheese.

Tax returns remain hidden, and thanks to the latest changes in taxation law, some of the highest-earning corporations paid no taxes in 2018. Some received refunds.

Immigrant children are not being "refunded" to their parents. Border Patrol, ICE, and Homeland Security agents close their ears to the tear-filled voices of mothers, fathers, and children who cry out to be reunited. They don't have to speak Spanish in order to understand words spoken in anguish every day.

The November 2020 election affords us one more opportunity to craft the ending we wish to see. I will vote for Joe Biden regardless of his age, race, or gender. Fifty-nine years after my birth, a coalition of intelligent Americans elected our first African American president. If I was able to wait that long for Americans to vote for intelligence and dignity, I can wait a bit longer for us to elect the first female president.

I do care about democracy in general and ours in particular. I'm fearful when I think I see the warning flags of autocratic fascism flapping in the air. I hope we can steer the nation toward civility and away from anger and hatred. I hope the night of November 3, 2020, or the days that follow will conclude like a classic romance novel filled with plot complications, strong characters, and a happily-ever-after ending.

TEMPORARILY DISCONNECTED

As much as I'd love to compose a blog post regarding one, single theme, I cannot seem to do it. I feel a kind of disconnection. Ten days ago, my sister and I held our frail, semi-conscious mother's hands in ours to assure her we were there in the hours before death took her. And so, I'm here, but not really here. I'm filling out forms and writing acknowledgment notes to our friends and those of our mother.

Disjointed memories flash through my brain as quickly as the pages of an early Walt Disney Studios' animator's drawings fall upon each other and become cartoons full of movement and color.

In the absence of organized sequential thoughts, I offer you, my readers, pieces of ephemera that have crossed my mind during these last weeks.

Meeting with the undertaker my mother selected years before her death was a unique experience. After a brief chat during which he played the "do you know so-and-so?" game, a guess-the-status strategy elevated to an art form by the generations-old rules of the Black Philadelphian haute bourgeoisie, the funeral director led my sister and me down a set of narrow, twisting stairs that took us to the funeral home's basement, now a casket showroom. Halfway through our descent, my sister hissed, "These are the stairs of death."

I agreed and immediately felt a twinge of guilt as irreverent thoughts crossed my mind. I gazed at the fleet of coffins on display. There was a 100% bronze beauty the undertaker labeled the "Michael Jackson model." I didn't ask why, because I didn't want to know the reason(s). There were several "ladies" models, so named because they had tufted satin linings embroidered with flowers. As the sales pitch continued, I waited for the funeral director to ask us, "What can I do to get your mother into one of these caskets today?" He didn't, thank God.

My mother had always made it clear that she didn't want to have a viewing. She considered it a barbaric practice. Her desire was to have the basic Episcopalian funeral mass, closed casket, of course.

So, you can imagine our distress when the funeral director seemed to forget that detail...several times.

F.D.: "She shouldn't wear the red dress you've selected. Everyone will focus on that and not on her face."

US: "The casket will be closed. No one will see her dress, no matter what color it is."

F.D.: "Oh, that's right. And please be sure all of her underwear is white."

Me: "Even if we *were* planning a viewing, who in God's name would be tugging on her dress and looking at her underwear?"

I don't recall his response. I'm pretty sure I blocked it from my memory.

My sister and I thought of a plan to ensure Mom's no-viewing edict would be followed. We planned to leap from our pew and grab the hands of any of the funeral director's assistants who even *looked like* they were going to open the casket. Thank goodness we didn't need to put that plan into action. It would not have been graceful.

Being in that beautiful Gothic church where I spent many Sunday mornings during my childhood and adolescence, seeing, hugging, and chatting with people I've known since forever but haven't seen for decades, reconnected me to the better moments of my past.

And now, although I know she's gone, I continue to worry about my mother because worry is one of the strands of my DNA's double helix.

Is my mom in pain? Is she warm enough? Can she swallow all of her meds? Does she remember I'm going to visit her tomorrow?

But I'm not going to visit her tomorrow, am I?

Before she returned to England, my sister went with me

to the county's office of the Register of Wills. We had to begin the Probate process. While we were there, I had the presence of mind to ask if we could meet Registrar D. Bruce Haines, Esq. I wanted to shake his hand and thank him for risking a jail sentence when he began issuing marriage licenses to same-gender couples in 2012, before it was legal to do so in Pennsylvania.

He was gracious and told me I'd given him a great way to start his day. I told him how much my spouse and I appreciated his bravery. He smiled and gazed at my sister and me.

"I believe he thinks we're the ones who are married," I said to her as we left the office.

"Yup," she responded and rolled her eyes, just as our mother would have done.

Writing has saved my spirit more than once, especially during the aftermath of sad episodes.

Because of its importance to me, there have been nights when I've looked up to the sky and whispered, "Mom, thanks for surrounding us with books, for introducing us to the magic of reading, and for acknowledging that I have a way with words."

It's doubtful that my sister and I could be the women we are today if we'd not experienced everything that was our mother during her yesterdays.

AT THE INTERSECTION OF SUPERHEROES AND ORANGE SODA

Or,

I'M IN A MEMOIR STATE OF MIND

Do retired surgeons ever bury their memories of hours spent in the O.R.? Can retired trial lawyers suppress their urge to mentally construct a defense or prosecution strategy when they read an account of a crime? Do writers ever cease imagining new characters and plots?

If you've been engaged in a career more than thirty years, it's mighty difficult to walk away and never look back.

I've heard you can take a teacher out of the classroom but you can't take the classroom out of the teacher. That seems truthful for me. The skills, relationships, and strategies I honed are still a part of me. The memories, both good and bad, persist.

Two Sundays ago, I heard the concern riding on the edge of my spouse's voice as she approached and held out a section of *The Philadelphia Inquirer*.

"Look at this," Viv said.

I glanced at the page's headline and then at the two photos posted beneath it.

A former colleague's image stared back at me. If her name hadn't been written under each photo, I would not have known who she was. How was it possible that I failed to recognize this person with whom I'd worked for so many years? How could it be that this perpetually physically fit former physical education teacher and dean of students was now shrouded in dementia?

I read about M.'s current struggles and about her daughter's sad challenges as she took charge of her mother's care. Having steered my own mother into a wonderful CCRC five years ago, and having witnessed her decline and death after suffering a tsunami-like stroke, I related to M.'s daughter's anguish.

As that Sunday wore on, I found myself skimming through the memory rolodex of my first two decades in the classroom. I remembered the ever-shifting emotions I'd experienced during the ups and downs of my first career. One profoundly low day involved M., the person whose photos were now in front of me. My feelings about one incident in particular were so deeply embedded in my mind that they played a role in my first and second books, *Leave of Absence* and *Breaking Jaie.*

I was walking down the steps, headed to the faculty lunchroom, when I noticed the clump of students gathered in the landing was larger and louder than usual. Suddenly I felt something cold and wet splash against my right leg.

A crescendo of screams arced through the air, and the mass of students' bodies grew thicker by the second. Whoops of excited delight muffled the static of a security person's walkie-talkie. The crowd shifted to the left and then to the right, like a swarm of starlings caught in opposing air currents.

That's when I witnessed a scene I could not have imagined, not in my wildest nightmares.

M. was on the floor. A female student sat astride her, powering her fists into M.'s upper torso and face. Someone reached through the chaos, pulled the student from atop M., and propelled her through a chorus of verbal approvals and fist pumps. In her wake, the assailant left profane screams and promises of killing M. the next "f...... time" she saw her.

The students who remained near the landing performed instant replays of the violence they'd just witnessed.

A non-teaching assistant retrieved M's twisted, broken eyeglasses from the corner where they'd landed.

I forgot about going to lunch and returned to my empty classroom.

That evening I tried to reconstruct what I wished had been only a horrible dream. I remembered feeling that cold liquid course down my leg and trickle into my shoe. I looked down and discovered I'd been hit by the contents of a can of orange soda, the orange soda M. tried to remove from the grip of the student who assaulted her. I replayed the beating M. had endured, and I cried. For the first time in my teaching career, I questioned whether I belonged in the classroom.

In the here and now, it's unlikely M. remembers that incident. If there are upsides to the disease of dementia, losing one's memory of a terrible incident must be at the top of the list.

I continued teaching for eighteen more years, long enough to experience many of its rewards. Among the positives are the moments when you learn about a student's successful ventures.

The same Sunday that I read about M., I read an interview in the *Philadelphia Gay News* titled, "Philly Actress Brings the 'Thunder' to Black Lightning."

A former student, Nafessa Williams, is in the throes of a successful acting career. Currently she's one of the protagonists in the CW Network series named above. Nafessa plays the role of Anissa/Thunder, television's first black lesbian superhero. A self-described anti-bullying activist and straight ally of the LGBTQ community, Nafessa attended ClexaCon in 2018. There she spoke with a young woman who tearfully thanked her for her portrayal of Anissa/Thunder.

"…after seeing Thunder, I feel normal for being a lesbian now," she said.

Many thanks to you, Nafessa. You've restored a young woman's belief in herself. Think about the other young women to whom you're giving strength and the courage to claim their identity.

If the trauma of having witnessed a coworker's beating had persuaded me to abandon working with kids who wanted to learn, students who stood up to violence and adversities every day of their young lives, I would not have received the gift of knowing so many young people who have found success and fulfillment as adults.

NEITHER A RANT NOR A RAVE

There's a literature-related issue about which I've had strong convictions for a long time, and I thought I'd raise the issue here.

When you write or read a novel, do you prefer stories devoid of politics or social problems? Or do you enjoy reading/writing books in which the characters and plot are engaged with sociopolitical issues? Perhaps you seek books that contain beautiful, skillfully written prose (art for the sake of art) *as well as* plots that explore social issues.

I prefer reading and writing the latter. I attribute my preference to experiences I had long ago during my college years. In one Spanish literature course, I encountered a professor who explained the personal and political messages concealed in Federico Garcia Lorca's poetry.

This instructor drew the lines that connected Lorca's symbolic imagery to the Spanish Civil War and then to the oppression of Spain's gay and educated, literary citizens. Seeing this connection made Lorca's work more accessible for me.

My second experience with politically engaged literature occurred when I encountered the works of the Negritude Movement (1950s). Immediately I saw its themes were the precursors to the poetry and prose of the 1960s-early1970s Black Arts Movement.

Most of the writers whose work reflected the momentum of those movements rejected the art-for-art's-sake credo and, instead, grabbed onto the belief that literature, along with the plastic arts, needed to be something that was functional. It had to be a body of work pulsating with life and inspiring change. At its very least, it had to examine society's sour notes.

Léopold Sédar Senghor and René Depestre (Negritude poets), Gwendolyn Brooks (whose work preceded the Black Arts Movement, but whose later poems embraced it), Nikki

Giovanni, Carolyn Rodgers, Don L. Lee, and Sonia Sanchez supported the premise that literature had the power to change people and socio-political systems. Sanchez celebrated her colleagues' talent for being "word sorcerers"* and opening the window so their readers could see the possibility of personal and political change.

The poetry that flowed from their pens was dynamic. Some of it was personal, devoted to private joys and lamentable heartbreak. All of it danced and jumped off the page. The gay and lesbian heirs of that movement, Audre Lorde, Alexis De Veaux, Joseph Beam, Jewelle Gomez, Essex Hemphill, Cheryl Clarke, and others have continued the tradition of creating "engaged literature."

Does my advocacy for literature with a function mean I'm campaigning for most novels to stimulate change or force feed our readers certain political messages? No, I'm not. I'm saying it's difficult for me to write a romance or mystery or literary fiction without creating characters who wrestle with any number of life's social issues. I prefer to write characters who confront ageism; racial discrimination; the inequities in education, employment, and health care; mental illness; misogyny; and homophobia. And I believe it's possible to write about these issues *and* create stories with realistic, pleasant endings.

I want my fiction to serve a purpose. I want my readers to enjoy the stories, but I also want them to be aware of matters with which perhaps, they've not had to contend.

Two topics that surfaced in my book, *The Rules,* were racial identity and the conflicts that are caused by colorism and class differences. These are well-known struggles enmeshed within the African American community, but they're painful problems we tend to keep to ourselves and not commit to a magnifying glass hovering above the pages of our books. With a few exceptions, (Michelle Cliff's *Abeng*) Black lesbian writers rarely include these topics in our stories. Perhaps claiming our sexuality, and writing about characters who own theirs, is a political act in itself. Exposing our "family secrets" is a bridge too far.

Can we create characters and plots that deal with social issues *and* offer our readers the sweet combo of entertainment and brain food they seek?

I believe we can. I believe we can offer stories with plot twists and turns, finely drawn characters whose flaws exist side by side with their better traits, who in the course of living their lives are forced to encounter some of the aforementioned issues.

I want to write books that serve a function beyond that of a reader's cocktail table decor-of-the-month. I seek to create books that entice readers to ponder historical, political, and social justice issues in general, and in particular, the role the reader plays relative to those issues. I want the fiction I write to serve a purpose, to engage the reader in thought. My work might not inspire my readers to dance, but I hope it will encourage them to think.

*"We Be Word Sorcerers," **Sonia Sanchez, Bantam Books, 1973**

RANDOMNESS

This month's post doesn't have a central theme. Why? Because I'm too distracted by *everything* that's swirling through the news. The impeachment non-trial, the Coronavirus pandemic, the Iowa Caucus Fail, and the political dominance of an ego-driven, bombastic man who puts his unrealistic policies before the preservation of our democracy. All of these distractions make it impossible for me to find one single theme about which to write. Therefore, what follows are a few **random** notes.

I've heard that **randomness** is a mathematical theory. Please don't ask me to understand or explain that theory. I'm an English and foreign language person whose brain's left and right hemisphere rarely work in tandem.

This just in to our news desk. Rush Limbaugh, having recently received the *Medal of Freedom,* is verbally attacking Mayor Pete Buttigieg for being gay and showing his affection toward his husband in full view of the public. Obviously, *freedom* has its limits.

I'm slightly freaked out by the daily infection and mortality rates related to Covid-19, so I thought it might be wise to order a box of medical-grade face masks. The only thing that stopped me from clicking Amazon's Place Order tab was the shipping cost. A box of twenty-five masks costs thirty dollars. The shipping fee is one hundred forty dollars. Huh? Where are these things manufactured? In China? Wait a minute...

As much as I enjoy reading general dramatic fiction written by and about lesbians, there are other books that remain lodged in my memory and stacked upon my   bookshelves simply because reading them made me laugh out loud. *How Firm a Foundation,* by Patrick Dennis, *Notes from a Small Island,* by Bill Bryson, *Rubyfruit Jungle*, by Rita Mae Brown, and *Cotillion,* by John Oliver Killens highlight some of life's absurdities and peoples' hypocrisies. The characters in these books act out the ironies of human behavior with crystal clarity. They poke fun of people we know. They poke fun of *us* and make us laugh at our own pretentiousness.

The 1960s TV series, *Rocky and Bullwinkle* as well as Mel Brooks's films, *Blazing Saddles* and *Young Frankenstein,* sharpened my appetite for political humor. The early Woody Allen (please don't hate me) flicks made me laugh at the foibles of incompetency.

Remember the dialogue between the bank teller and the pseudo-bank robber in *Take the Money and Run?*

"What? You have a gub? Harry, this guy says he wants money and he has a gub. I don't know what he's talking about. Could you come look at this note?"

The song, "Rebels Are We" in the film *Bananas* highlights empty-headed mob allegiance to corrupt, egocentric leaders. Hmmm...

Picture the angry, torch-bearing townspeople as they made their way to the castle in *Young Frankenstein.* That scene of people yelling and wanting to attack "the creature" reminds me of other similarly motivated marches. Namely, the infamous KKK march in Washington, D.C. and the more recent white-supremacists' torch-lit, "you will not replace us" march in Charlottesville, VA. Angry/fearful white men, torches, yelling...the whole nine yards.

I'm seriously addicted to *The Late Show with Stephen Colbert.* Colbert's monologues filter the day's insane moments and soundbites and reassure me that some people are still in touch with our nation's kinder, more civil reality. Colbert's nightly comments shine a spotlight on the most recent examples of that which is profane, hateful, stupid, and ridiculous. Thank goodness!

A U.S. president who tweets misspelled words is really a reprise of Woody Allen's "gub."

A political rally filled with people who seem bereft of a single independent thought as they chant, "Lock her up!" is not very different from the angry villagers in *Young Frankenstein, n'est-ce pas?*

According to Wikipedia and IMdB, between 2008 and 2016, thirty-one filmmakers produced thirty-one movies about slavery. Why was there a resurgence of interest in enslavement during that time period? Spoiler alert! Who was president of the United States? Coincidence? I think not.

Two final thoughts from Randomville...

Now that I'm older, my prescription meds bottles arrive with child-proof caps. Is BigPharma trying to trick me into maintaining my manual dexterity, or are they attempting to rush me into the arms of an additional medication, one that will control my frustration?

Holding on to our sense of humor will help us get through and over these troubling times. That, and charting how many times Stephen Colbert unbuttons and rebuttons his jacket during any random evening can strengthen our resolve to resist that which is indefensible.

ELEVEN "WHAT IF'S?"

Happy New Year already! Enough with resolutions that fade away as quickly as spent firecrackers. Instead, how about a few "what if's"? Who doesn't enjoy the indulgence of daydreaming?

What if...

- we selected one item of clothing a day for the next seven days, put the clothing in a box, and donated those clothes to a shelter for the homeless?

- when passing by strangers burdened with surly or unhappy facial expressions, we smiled and said "Hello!"

- we contacted someone we haven't talked to in a long while, perhaps a childhood friend? "Hi, Martha!" "Hello, Kathleen!"

- we held the door open for those behind us, regardless of their age, gender, or race, or of ours?

- we admitted we MUST talk about our nation's legacy of enslavement and the price we continue to pay because we've never talked about it honestly, one on one or group to group? And what if we **listened** to each other instead of talking **at** each other?

- we held each other blameless for the cruelties of the past, but held each other responsible for understanding the cellular-level pain that accompanies the ever-present ejections, along with the underestimations of character, intellect, and ability that many of us continue to experience?

- we proudly claimed our demographic identities pertaining to age, gender, race, religious affiliation, sexuality, profession, socio-economic status, political leanings, and geographic location but **refused** to be boxed in by those descriptors?

- we rejected being told for whom we're expected to vote because we're: college-educated, suburban, white women/ Southern black men/LGBTQIA/women/millennials/baby boomers/X-geners/blue-collar, straight, white males/middle- of-the-road, mid-westerners/uber-wealthy corporate execs/ latinxs/Evangelicals?

- trump had paid attention in January 2020 when his advisors warned him about the coming pandemic?

- we went to the polls this spring and next fall, shrugged off every expectation placed upon our demographic group, and voted for the preservation of: our democracy, decency, humanitarianism, and the candidate who possesses the intellectual capacity, empathy, and self-expressive skills beyond that of a five-year-old child?

- all of the above were reality and not simply "what if" daydreams?

EXCUSE ME WHILE I BURN A FEW BRIDGES

People, we have a huge problem more insidious than COVID-19. It's a virus that's been dividing us and replicating itself during the course of four centuries. And yes, this is a blog about racism. If you're tired of reading about this topic, stop right here. If you're curious, keep going.

I don't know if this is true for you, but the older I become, the more I want to learn. I have so many unasked questions. Some may sound naïve or childlike, but I assure you, I'm asking from a place of sincere curiosity.

For those of you who are historians, when and where did so many white people first have a negative visceral reaction to black people? Did this negative reaction feel like fear, loathing, anger? We need to talk about this.

For the psychologists in our midst, why did/does fear express itself as an aggressive need to belittle, destroy, or dominate those who are feared? Why, in spite of truths to the contrary, do some white people continue to believe they are superior in every way to people of color? We need to have several conversations about this.

From my perspective, there are as many threads woven into racism as there are in the AIDS Quilt. Because I steer my boat toward pragmatism, and because racism is so pervasive, I figure it's best to tackle this dilemma one thread at a time. The thread that comes to mind in this setting is the one tenuously connecting lesbian literature to ALL of its writers, readers, and producers. This thread is thin and it's fraying, especially for the forty-year-olds and up among us. We've stood on a few bridges far too long.

Here's the first bridge to which I bring a torch.

If you're a publisher, how many books written by writers of color (WOC) have you published? How many content editors, copy editors, book cover artists, promotion-tasked folks of color have you employed? Do you accept or reject book covers that reveal the protagonists are POC? How many minority-owned bookstores/book clubs/book fairs do you contact in an effort to promote the books you publish? How many manuscripts written by authors of color have you rejected because of the manuscripts' characters of color, not because of the quality of the work? Can we please talk about this?

On a personal note, there's an issue that continues to smolder under my feet. My first book was self-published. The manuscript for my second book was praised for its literary merit but rejected by a lesbian-owned publishing house because "no one will be interested in reading about a black girl's coming out." That happened only thirteen years ago, not during the Jim Crow era.

Please know these names:

Stephanie A. Allen,
Nikki Baker,
LaShonda Barnett,
Samiya Bashir,
Renée Bess,
Becky Birtha,
Dionne Brand,
Sharon Bridgforth,
Laurinda Brown,
Shonia Brown,
Octavia Butler.

Onto the next bridge that awaits immolation.

If you're a lesfic reader, have you bought any books written by WOC? When you're shopping for books online or in person, do you tend to pass by those whose covers illustrate characters of color? When you've read books authored by WOC, have you felt surprised to discover the characters and plot details might represent life experiences that differ from yours, but the themes are universal? We need to listen to each other about this issue.

Please get acquainted with these names:

Staceyann Chin,

Cheril N. Clarke,
Cheryl Clarke,
Michelle Cliff,
Lucille Clifton,
Angela Davis,
Alexis De Veaux,
Alice Dunbar-Nelson,
Mari Evans,
Jessie Fauset,
Jewelle Gomez,
Sheree L. Greer,
Angelina Weld Grimké,
Alexis Pauline Gumbs,
Rosa Guy.

And now, as gently as I can, I'll strike a match and set it down on this last bridge, a bridge upon which I've seen a few WOC stand quietly, as if they're asking permission to offer the world diverse characters, as if writing about white characters *only* will ensure greater book sales and faster popularity.

The lane markings on this bridge are faded. Its signage and support columns are rusted and weakened by the passage of time and the progress we've made. Why not write your reality? Why not write stories about the range of black peoples' experiences? Why write your books for the white gaze only?

Those of us who grew up in racially diverse communities, attended schools with students of different races and ethnicities, and as adults entered interracial relationships/marriages know first-hand the complexities, subtle or not, of the gumbo in which we exist. We are constantly aware of how the world sees and perceives us. Our survival depends upon that awareness. I'm suggesting there's a readership eager to meet all kinds of characters of color and explore their stories.

Please read these names.

Lorraine Hansberry,
Nikki Harmon,
JP Howard,
Cheryl Head,
Bell Hooks,

Zora Neale Hurston,
N. K. Jemisin,
June Jordan,
Gayle Jones,
Nella Larson,
Ana-Maurine Lara,
Audre Lorde,
Penny Mickelbury,
Mia McKenzie,
Lisa C. Moore,
Nik Nicholson,
Chinelo Okparanta,
Pat Parker,
Nikki Rashan,
Sapphire,
Ann Allen Shockley,
Makeda Silvera,
Barbara Smith,
Linda Villarosa,
Alice Walker,
Ida B. Wells,
Rebekah Weatherspoon,
Anondra Williams,
KD Williamson,
Jacqueline Woodson,
Shay Youngblood,
Fiona Zedde.

We cannot continue to fear, fight, and diminish one another while # 45 draws targets on our backs and the reality of eight minutes, forty-six seconds assaults us head-on.

*My sincerest apologies to any lesbian writer of color whose name I've not included.

In memory of Sherry Mills who always sought to help people, no matter their race, gender identity, age, or sexuality. We miss you, Sherry.

About the Author

Renée Bess, a former teacher, began writing in earnest after her short story, "At the Beauty Parlor," won first place in a Philadelphia area literary contest.

Her novels, *Leave of Absence, Breaking Jaie, RE:Building Sasha, The Butterfly Moments,* and *The Rules,* published by Regal Crest Enterprises, explore the genres of romance with intrigue, and general dramatic fiction. Renée and Lee Lynch co-curated *Our Happy Hours, LGBT Voices from the Gay Bars,* an anthology of short fiction, memoirs, and poetry which won the Golden Crown Literary Society's 2018 Anthology Award. She is so proud to be one of the four recipients of the 2019 Alice B. Readers Awards.

Renée remains committed to writing stories that include diverse characters, cogent social themes, and well-crafted language.

Web site: www.reneebess.com

Books by Renée Bess

Leave of Absence

Corey Lomax, a writer and English professor at Allerton University in suburban Philadelphia, continues to recover from the rupture of a six year relationship with Jennifer Renfrew, the university's Assistant Dean of Admissions. Jennifer has embarked on a new relationship with Pat Adamson, a Philadelphia police officer.

Kinshasa Jordan, a novelist and teacher on leave from her public high school position in Connecticut, accepts a writer-in-residence post at Allerton. When she relocates, Kinshasa leaves behind a secure job as well as an abusive relationship.

Corey and Kinshasa meet as colleagues, writers, and minority women who must navigate their way through the sometimes unfriendly territory of white male dominated academia. Corey is proudly "out." Kinshasa's sexuality is a matter of conjecture. What is clear is both Corey's and Kinshasa's determination to avoid any romantic entanglements.

As the story unfolds, so do secrets, betrayals, a murder, and the slowly smoldering attraction between Corey Lomax and Kinshasa Jordan.

ISBN 978-1-61929-106-5
eISBN 978-1-61929-107-2

Breaking Jaie

Jaie Baxter, an African-American Ph.D candidate at Philadelphia's Allerton University, is determined to win a prestigious writing grant. In order to win the Adamson Grant, Jaie initially plans to take advantage of one of the competition's judges, Jennifer Renfrew, who is also a University official. Jennifer has spent the past ten years alone following the murder of her lover, Patricia Adamson, in whose honor the grant is named. Jennifer is at first susceptible to Jaie's flirtation, but is later vengeful when she discovers the real reason for Jaie's sudden romantic interest in her. A lunch with an old cop friend reveals that Jaie may very well have ties to Adamson's death.

Jaie is confronted with painful memories as she prepares an autobiographical essay for the grant application. She recalls the emotional trauma of her older brother's death, the murder of a police detective, her dismissal from her "dream" high school, and her victimization at the hands of hateful homophobic students. She remembers her constant struggles with her mother's alcohol-fueled jealousies and physical abuse she had to endure. This wake-up call causes her to look at her life in new ways.

But Jaie is not the only student applying for the grant. Terez Overton, a wealthy Boston woman, is Jaie's chief competitor. Jaie is drawn to the New Englander immediately but is also unnerved by her. She has no clue that Terez is trying to decide whether she wants to accept an opportunity to write an investigative article about an unsolved murder. Writing that article could put her budding relationship with Jaie in jeopardy.

And just when the angst of old memories and the uncertainty of her future with Terez are complicating Jaie's life, her manipulative ex, Seneca Wilson, returns to Philadelphia to reclaim Jaie using emotional blackmail.

Senecas actions serve to wound and break Jaie in many ways. Will Seneca drive the final wedge between Jaie and Terez? Who will win the Adamson grant? And what did Jaie have to do with the death of Patricia Adamson?

eISBN 978-1-932300-84-0 (Released in eBook formats Only)

Re: Building Sasha

Sasha Lewis, the uber-competent manager of Willingham Builders, is drowning in a whirlpool of distrust as she struggles to maintain her relationship with Lee Simpson, her dangerously twisted unfaithful lover. In a self-imposed exile from most of her friends, Sasha recalls a brief work related encounter with Avery Sloan; an encounter destined to become more meaningful when Avery's social service agency hires Whittingham Builders to convert an old Victorian era house to a residence for former offenders.

How far will Lee take her cheating? How much emotional damage will Sasha endure before she begins to rebuild her spirit? Will Sasha grab Avery's outstretched hand and accept the gentle yet exciting offer of love she sees in this woman?

ISBN 978-1-935053-07-1
eISBN 978-1-61929-034-1

The Butterfly Moments

After a twenty-plus year career as a Parole Officer in Philadelphia, Alana Blue is more than ready to leave her job and move on to more rewarding work. Jaded and burned out, Alana is given the difficult assignment of supervising Rafe Ortiz, a renegade Probation and Parole Officer who arrives in Alana's office by way of a disciplinary transfer and with a reputation for accumulating meaningless sexual conquests.

Alana's life is more complicated by the frequent conflicts she experiences with her homophobic daughter, Nikki. Convinced that the transparency of her mother's sexuality doomed her first marriage, Nikki is obsessed with keeping her second union intact, even if it means constantly repudiating Alana. Nikki's husband, Owen Reid, doesn't always agree with his wife's opinions regarding same-gender relationships; nor does he always support their marriage by remaining faithful to Nikki.

As Alana is reaching for an opportunity to pursue a new career, the body of a brutally murdered university student is discovered partially hidden on a property very close to Alana's neighborhood. Detective Johnetta Jones, recently retired from the Philadelphia Police Force, and hired by a suburban law enforcement department, is assigned to the murder case. When the investigation leads her to one of Alana's parolees, Johnetta remembers having interviewed this particular Parole Officer once before. Although her memory of Alana is mostly pleasant, Johnetta remains more emotionally connected to her work than she is to any woman she's ever met. Vaguely discontent, she is reluctant to forge a romantic connection with anyone...until her path intersects with Alana's once again. Their renewed contact suggests the possibility of love and the end of loneliness for both women. As Johnetta and her work partner, Detective Harold Smythe, get close to solving the university student's murder, Johnetta realizes arresting their suspect will imperil her tenuous relationship with Alana.

Alana becomes caught in the war between her impulsive attraction to Rafe Ortiz's flirtatious pursuit and her realization that her feelings for Johnetta Jones are growing deeper with each passing day. Will everything in Alana's world disintegrate when lies are revealed, true identities are exposed, and the murderer is unmasked?

ISBN 978-1-935053-37-8
eISBN 978-1-935053-37-8

The Rules

Blackmail, murder, missing persons, and hidden identities link lives that otherwise, would have remained unconnected.

London Phillips' suburban black middle class background has made her vulnerable to the alienation she feels as she tap dances between the expectations she holds for herself and the expectations other people impose upon her. A full-time realtor and part-time writer, London encounters frustration when she tries to contact Milagros Farrow, a revered lesbian author whose work London would like to include in an anthology she's compiling. Milagros has disappeared from the face of the earth.

Rand Carson is a prominent newspaper journalist who is forced to deal with the sudden loss of her financial security and the dissolution of her long term interracial relationship with Willa. Rand seems compelled to pursue London, although it's possible she's more attracted to London's ethnicity than to London herself.

Candace Dickerson, a corporate event planner, is married to avarice. In order to chase a more lucrative future, Candace has abandoned her lover, Lenah and Lenah's perceived lack of ambition. She's moved into the city where she executes a plot designed to augment her earnings with other people's money.

Lenah Miller is content with her job at a local hospital's Emergency Department. For reasons known only to her, she distrusts women she considers too ambitious or from different social strata. Steeped in cynicism and memories held in secret, Lenah finds it easier to criticize a woman whose gentle nature differs from hers than to accept their differences.

The threads entwined around London's desire to connect with a kindred spirit, Lenah's wary skepticism,

Rand's inappropriate ardor, and Candace's greed come undone when three people fall victim to blackmail, one reappears, and another succumbs to murder.

ISBN 978-1-61929-156-0
eISBN 978-1-61929-157-7

Our Happy Hours:
LGBT Voices From the Gay Bars

During the days and nights following the massacre at the Pulse Nightclub in Orlando, Florida, the world listened as various spokespersons attempted to explain to the general public exactly what the gay bar/club meant to LGBTQI people. The words "safe place," "refuge," "free to be ourselves" flew through the air.

We queer writers grappled with the tragedy alongside our brothers and sisters. How could we express our feelings about the places where we could drop all pretense of conforming to the hetero-normative society's rules? What words could we gather to let the rest of the world know the pain we felt upon losing so many beautiful strangers on a night in June and in a place that had been one of our havens?

How and why does the gay bar intersect so many of our lives?

The stories and poems living between the covers of this book attempt to answer those questions. Spend a few happy hours with us in our gay bars.

ISBN 978-1-63304-813-3 (Paper Back)
ISBN 237-0-00059-493-8 (Hard Back)
eISBN 978-1-63304-804-1

Bringing LGBTQAI+ Stories to Life

Visit us at our website: www.flashpointpublications.com

CPSIA information can be obtained
at www.ICGtesting.com
Printed in the USA
BVHW040311240221
600911BV00010B/510